CW00797564

Quarterly Essay

Quarterly Essay is published four times a year by Black Inc., an imprint of Schwartz Books Pty Ltd. Publisher: Morry Schwartz.

ISBN 9781760642907 ISSN 1832-0953

Subscriptions – 1 year print & digital (4 issues): $79.95 within Australia incl. GST. Outside Australia $119.95. 2 years print & digital (8 issues): $149.95 within Australia incl. GST. 1 year digital only: $49.95.

Payment may be made by Mastercard or Visa, or by cheque made out to Schwartz Books. Payment includes postage and handling.

To subscribe, fill out and post the subscription card or form inside this issue, or subscribe online:

quarterlyessay.com
subscribe@blackincbooks.com
Phone: 61 3 9486 0288

Correspondence should be addressed to:

The Editor, Quarterly Essay
Level 1, 221 Drummond Street
Carlton VIC 3053 Australia
Phone: 61 3 9486 0288 / Fax: 61 3 9011 6106
Email: quarterlyessay@blackincbooks.com

Editor: Chris Feik. Management: Elisabeth Young. Publicity: Anna Lensky. Design: Guy Mirabella. Assistant Editor: Kirstie Innes-Will. Production Coordinator: Marilyn de Castro. Typesetting: Tristan Main.

Printed in Australia by McPherson's Printing Group. The paper used to produce this book comes from wood grown in sustainable forests.

| GETTING | Australia's Energy |
| TO ZERO | Transition |

Alan Finkel

"You never change things by fighting the existing reality. To change
something, build a new model that makes the existing model obsolete."

—Buckminster Fuller

PLANNED OBSOLESCENCE

Like others, I dream that my great-grandchildren, whom I might never
meet, will grow up living on a planet just as magnificent as it was when
I was young. Fulfilment of this dream will require that we preserve our
planet's unique beauty in the face of global warming, armed with ambition
and realism. We do not have time for fatalism or despair.

Achieving net-zero emissions will be difficult, but is not impossible. We
cannot simply shut down the use of fossil fuels overnight, because our
civilisation needs energy. Instead, we must harness science and technology
to develop alternatives that make fossil fuels obsolete. We must replace our
nineteenth-century energy sources with 21st-century alternatives: low-
emissions technologies that will undo the problems wrought by the
high-emissions incumbents. Technology to solve technology's problems.

This will take an adaptive, technology-based plan to maintain our quality of living and reap the benefits of the transition.

The plan will involve a massive global commitment to solar, wind and hydro (and, in some countries, nuclear) electricity, to transmission lines and storage, distributed generation and variable loads. We will need to change the way we farm food and process it, our vehicles and transport systems, our building designs and heating and cooling systems, our industrial processes. And we will need effective, affordable geosequestration and biosequestration to deal with the hard-to-abate emissions that will remain with us despite all these efforts.

A meeting of the minds is required, so that we can use tools that are good, but not perfect, to accelerate the transformation. For most of us, the motivation for a switch to clean energy is to mitigate climate change. That is reason enough. But shifting to a net-zero-emissions economy has other advantages. It will rid us of our dependence on a finite resource – fossil fuels – and it will ensure better air quality, cheaper energy, and participation in a global economic transformation. Thus, even those who are not convinced about the threat posed by climate change should be enthusiastic about the transformations that are underway and contemplated, because they will ultimately contribute to prosperity, new exports and a healthier environment.

We are in the early stages of an energy revolution. The industrial revolution began with the use of coal to create steam for industry and for locomotion. Note, though, that coal did not replace the use of wood, dried manure and other biomass for heating. Instead, it massively expanded energy use. Along came oil. It eventually displaced the use of coal for locomotion in trains and ships, but not for steam and electricity production. Along came natural gas. It eventually displaced the use of town gas made from coal, and much of the use of oil for heating, but not for transport and electricity production. Since the start of the industrial age, these three fossil fuels – coal, oil and natural gas – have added to our total fuel use rather than replacing the old. This additive adoption of new fuels has resulted in greenhouse gas emissions increasing year after year.

The latest energy revolution, already underway, is different. Electricity from renewable energy (and in some countries from nuclear) will eventually completely replace all three fossil fuels as energy sources. Oil and natural gas will likely remain as chemical feedstocks in some manufacturing, but their use as a fuel will fade into obsolescence. The burning questions are: how long will that take? Can we accelerate the process? Can we do so while reaping economic benefits and creating new jobs to replace the old?

This essay traces a pathway to a clean-energy future for Australia, a crucially important task that I began to dabble in before my five-year term as Australia's chief scientist began, and which turned out to be a major component of my work in that role, way beyond anything I imagined when I started. I tackle some of the controversial and difficult questions, such as the role of natural gas in the coming decades, and share some confounding personal moments from Australia's recent climate debate. But my overarching thesis is that just as nineteenth-century technology has brought us to an urgent moment in the history of our planet, 21st-century technology will light the way forward.

Change is in the air. The global momentum and enthusiasm for solar and wind as our future primary energy sources, supported by big batteries, hydrogen, other storage technologies, distributed energy generation, managed loads and digital technologies, across all sectors of our economy, including transport and industry, is growing every day. I sense we will live through a technological revolution this decade as exciting as the conquest of space in the 1960s.

If Australia handles the challenge well, we can build an economy that takes advantage of the transition. If we cling to the past, we will miss opportunities that the rest of the world will seize. The last thing we want is to be cave dwellers, watching the future march back and forth outside the cave opening. The scale of the job is vast and it will take decades. But we must be part of the revolution rather than left behind. As the Borg said in *Star Trek: The Next Generation*: "Resistance is futile."

GLOBAL WARMING: SOME FACTS

Global warming is real and anthropogenic – caused by humans. Our planet is overheating because of greenhouse gas emissions associated with modern civilisation. The consequence is a changing climate.

This reality is made abundantly clear by temperature graphs. As Figure 1 shows, Australia's average air temperature has risen 1.4°C since national records began in 1910. And the past decade was hot. Really hot. In fact, a ten-year-old in Australia today has already lived through eight of the hottest years in our recorded history.

Figure 1: *Temperature rise since 1910 in Australia*

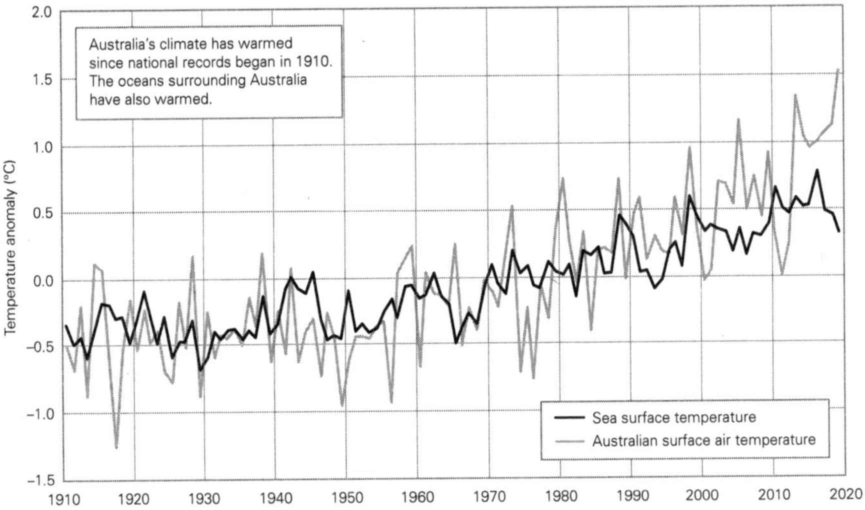

Source: CSIRO and BOM, *State of the Climate 2020.*
Note: Baseline averaging period is 1960–1991.

Globally, 2020 was equal-hottest, along with 2016 and 2019. The average global temperature was 1.2°C warmer than the pre-industrial (1850–1900) level, closing in on the Paris Agreement's preferred limit of 1.5°C.

Significant as that warming of the atmosphere is, the biggest heat absorption has been in the oceans. Of the extra heat trapped by the added greenhouse gases, approximately 90 per cent has accumulated in the oceans, owing to their high surface area, low reflectivity, and higher density and heat capacity relative to air.

Changing sea levels confirm the warming of the planet. Over most of the past century, they rose at an average rate of 1.4 millimetres per year. Between 2006 and 2015, this rate increased to 3.6 millimetres per year. The rise in sea levels is attributed partly to the thermal expansion of seawater as it warms, and partly to the net melting of land ice, such as ice sheets and glaciers.

Both theory and experimental physics make the case that the driver of this global warming trend is the increased concentration of greenhouse gases in the atmosphere. Our understanding of this process dates back almost 200 years, to 1824, when a gifted French mathematician, Joseph Fourier, whose work continues to underpin modern telecommunications, medical imaging and many branches of engineering, asked a simple question: what is regulating Earth's temperature? Fourier theorised that the atmosphere was keeping the Earth's surface warm, like the glass windows in a greenhouse – hence the term "the greenhouse effect."

In 1896, a Swedish chemist named Svante Arrhenius went a step further and determined the underlying physics of global warming. Arrhenius's explanation was that the visible light from the sun striking the Earth's surface warms it, and some of the heat is emitted in a different form, known as infrared radiation. Ordinarily, this infrared radiation would escape to space. However, through his lab-bench experiments, Arrhenius found that some gases, including carbon dioxide, trap this infrared radiation and re-emit it in all directions. While some of that re-emitted infrared radiation makes its way back into space, the rest warms the Earth's atmosphere, surface and oceans beyond their natural levels.

We depend on these greenhouse gases to support all life on Earth. Without them, the Earth would lose so much heat that the average global temperature would be −18°C and life as we know it would be impossible.

We humans and other mammals are much happier with the actual average global temperature of 15°C! We are well adapted to this average temperature, so it is a problem when greenhouse gas levels rise because of human activity, trapping too much of the sun's energy as heat. This is referred to as the "enhanced" greenhouse effect.

To see the trend of the past fifty years, we only have to take a trip to the rugged cliffs of Cape Grim, at the north-western tip of Tasmania. This is an area known for rich soil, abundant rainfall and the roar of strong westerly winds that crash into the coastline after a journey thousands of kilometres across the Indian Ocean. These factors combine to make Cape Grim the perfect place to sample two things: some of the world's finest beef and some of the world's most pristine and well-mixed air, which the CSIRO and Bureau of Meteorology began to do in 1976.

The message these air samples carry is indeed grim. There are many greenhouse gases, but the two most significant are carbon dioxide and methane, in that order. As Figure 2 shows, in each of the forty-five years

Figure 2: Carbon dioxide and methane curves at Cape Grim

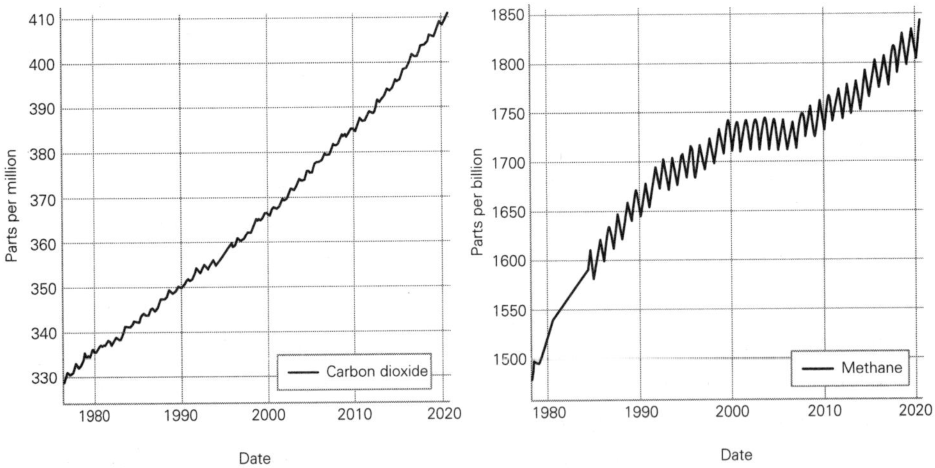

Source: CSIRO.

since record-keeping began the carbon dioxide concentration has risen. I've often looked at this graph, eagerly hoping to see a downturn. It's not there. Even the economic hit from the COVID-19 pandemic has not been enough to slow it. The gradient of the atmospheric concentration of methane is more variable than the carbon dioxide curve, but the trend is also upwards.

The same trend is seen for the past sixty-two years in the measurements from the Mauna Loa Observatory, high on the slopes of Hawaii's largest volcano. The annual carbon dioxide fluctuations are due to the photosynthetic activity of plants in the Northern Hemisphere, which has more land plants than the Southern Hemisphere. The annual methane fluctuations are due to several factors, including temperature-dependent releases from wetlands.

*

A brief digression on carbon dioxide: it is not a pollutant. Calling it a pollutant runs the risk of trivialising the toxic effects of true pollutants. Carbon dioxide is not toxic. It is a product of human metabolism and we exhale it at more than 100 times higher concentration than is found in the atmosphere. In the reverse cycle, plants absorb carbon dioxide to use as the feedstock for photosynthesis. Carbon dioxide is a fundamental part of our lifecycle, but it also happens to be a greenhouse gas.

At the start of the industrial revolution, the concentration of carbon dioxide was 278 parts per million. Today, the concentration is 411 parts per million, a level not experienced for 4 million years. And there is absolutely no hint of a slowdown. Annual carbon dioxide emissions from human activities increased from 24 billion tonnes in 1998 to 37 billion tonnes in 2018. Some who wish it were not so dismiss the measurements of global temperature, carbon dioxide and methane gas as a conspiracy by scientists, journalists, bankers, activists and young people. All I can say on that score is that the notion of a conspiracy of this size and consistency is absurd.

Two other flawed arguments are sometimes offered. The first is that the percentage of carbon dioxide is so small that it couldn't make a difference.

In percentage terms, carbon dioxide is just over 0.04 per cent of the atmosphere. It's true, that is small, but the physical mechanisms discovered by Arrhenius and many generations of physicists show that it is enough to affect temperature. Take a look beyond Earth and the significance of carbon dioxide as a greenhouse gas is readily apparent. Unsurprisingly, the average temperature of the planets in our solar system drops off with distance from the sun. There is one exception: Venus, which, although it is further from the sun than Mercury, is hotter than Mercury because of its predominantly carbon dioxide atmosphere.

In 1896, Arrhenius calculated that if the concentration of atmospheric carbon dioxide were doubled, the average temperature would increase by between 5°C and 6°C. The much more intensive analysis done by modern computer modelling puts the impact of doubling at between 2.6°C and 3.9°C.

The second flawed argument is that the increase is natural, and that such increases have happened in the past. Well, not for 4 million years, and never at the incredible pace seen today. Confirmation that the increase is primarily from burning fossil fuels comes from multiple lines of evidence: the decreasing proportion of the Carbon-13 isotope compared with the Carbon-12 isotope in the atmosphere and oceans (because fossil fuels contain proportionately less Carbon-13 than the atmosphere); the observed dominance of these isotopic ratio changes in the Northern Hemisphere, where most fossil fuel emissions occur; a decrease in oxygen in the atmosphere that mirrors the increase in carbon dioxide; and analyses of historical emissions.

This is the message from the overwhelming majority of the evidence, but the science is hefty and at times complex. It is not easy to explain in Senate estimates committee hearings. I recall one exchange with Senator Malcolm Roberts, who asked me in 2017, "Are you aware of Richard Feynman and his quote, 'A beautiful theory is shot down by an ugly fact?'" As I understood Senator Roberts, he was suggesting that the theory of global warming should be torpedoed by anomalous temperature data that doesn't match the trend. His quote is actually from Thomas Huxley, who in 1870 delivered an excellent exposition of 200 years of scientific efforts to understand how life is generated, as experiments were devised and refined. Huxley was describing the scientific method in action.

I responded to Senator Roberts with a quote of my own, from Michael Faraday, who (to my imperfect recollection at the time) had said, "I hold my most valued theory at the tips of my fingers so that the most gentle breeze can blow it away." Faraday's point was that a fundamental of science is that if a contradictory fact appears, you must question and check your theory, and, if necessary, be prepared to discard it and come up with a better one. Scientific theories are validated or disproved by experiments, and good theories stand up to repeated and varied experiments. That doesn't mean every single experiment or every single data point will agree. But a theory becomes more robust the more experiments that are done and the more datasets that support it. It becomes the best theory we have in answer to a specific problem, within a certain degree of probability. And so a consensus develops. This is the scientific method.

The theory that the global temperature is warming due to human activity is so extensively supported by theory, laboratory experiments and reams of data that it can be considered incontrovertible. That doesn't mean the temperature next year can be accurately predicted. Just as for the weather forecast, there is variability. But the trends are predictable, and when we look at trends rather than individual measurements we find no ugly facts to slay the theory of global warming. Despite scientists being prepared to let go if there is a breath of contrary fact, there has been no need to do so.

Unfortunately, it does not take a lot of warming for our climate to be affected, and no nation is immune. Indeed, many nations that contribute the least are facing the most serious consequences. Because ocean currents and major wind patterns respond to warming, a temperature rise of just 1°C can cause major disruptions to the natural systems that regulate our climate, as predicted by the increasingly sophisticated computer models used to construct future scenarios.

The accuracy of any model depends on the sophistication of the algorithms and the quality of the data. When models are used to extrapolate into the future using simple algorithms and poor datasets, they can lead to implausible predictions, as we saw in the early days of modelling the COVID-19 pandemic. The accuracy of the pandemic modelling improved markedly as scientists developed more sophisticated models and gained access to much larger real-world datasets of transmission patterns.

Importantly, our climate models are far more advanced than pandemic modelling. They are impressive, and that is because they are built on hypotheses debated and refined for thirty years, and credible data from billions of data points around the planet over many decades of recording.

One way to test their accuracy is to apply the modern models to datasets from decades past to see whether they predict the current climate. They do. They reproduce observed historical climate trends when they include the effects of increased greenhouse gases in the atmosphere. They fail to reproduce the observed trends when they only include natural factors such as solar output and volcanic activity.

Global warming is replete with contradictory effects. For example, water vapour emitted by jet planes in the stratosphere is a potent greenhouse gas, so it contributes to global warming. However, to the extent that it contributes to cloud formation, it increases the Earth's albedo, causing more sunlight to be reflected back into space, thereby partially negating the global warming impact. Similarly, particle and aerosol pollutants from industrial processes block sunlight and contribute to global cooling, also known as global dimming, again negating to some extent the warming impact of increasing carbon dioxide levels. The models used by scientists take into account all the known factors, including these.

Should we simply learn to live with climate change? Absolutely not. Just 200 years ago our ancestors were the custodians of a pristine planet. Through burning fossil fuels and biomass, we visibly ruined the air quality with particulates, sulphur emissions and nitrogen oxides. In many countries, we have dramatically reversed that decline in air quality. But

Figure 3: Number of extreme heat events in Australia, 1910–2018

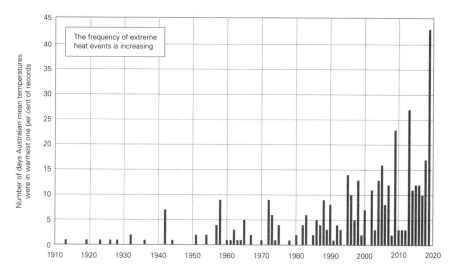

Source: CSIRO and BOM, *State of the Climate 2020.*

an invisible enemy remains: greenhouse gas emissions. The harm they do is slower to develop, and indirect, but increases in some weather extremes – such as extreme heat events (see Figure 3) and fire weather (meteorological conditions conducive to fires starting and spreading rapidly) – are already discernible in Australia. The widespread and devastating bushfires of 2019 and 2020 in California and Australia showed this all too clearly.

Globally, there is evidence of increasingly intense storms and cyclones, disrupted rainfall patterns, deeper droughts, more frequent extreme fire weather and longer fire seasons, sea-level rises, larger coastal storm surges, ocean acidification and erratic swings in coastal water temperatures and consequent coral bleaching.

In the most extreme case, the risks might be substantially worse than most people expect. One horror scenario starts in the tundras of Siberia, Canada and Alaska. There, frozen in the permafrost, vast quantities of methane clathrate are stored. What is methane clathrate? It is methane gas trapped at high concentration in a crystal structure of water. The quantities of methane trapped in the permafrost and deep ocean sediments exceed the energy equivalent of the known reserves of oil, coal and shale combined. The scary possibility is that as the global temperature rises, the permafrost will melt. Already, many surfaces in Siberia, a region bigger than France and Germany combined, have turned from hard frozen soil to shallow pools. In some areas, bubbles of methane gas have been observed; whether or not these are new or background phenomena remains a focus of research. The reason for concern is that methane is a greenhouse gas twenty-eight times more potent than carbon dioxide. The nightmare prospect is that as the temperature rises, methane will bubble into the atmosphere, where its presence would cause the global average temperature to rise faster and release more methane even faster than before. It could become a runaway phenomenon. Although resourceful humans will learn to live with and manage climate change, albeit at great cost, this type of scenario might put us into a situation where the environment would be changing so fast that the disruptive pressures on our society could be overwhelming. Whether or not such a tipping point could occur, or instead might be compensated by other environmental responses, is the subject of much debate and research, but it would be better not to run the field experiment.

There are always counterarguments to the gloomy forecasts. For example, there is some possibility that elevated carbon dioxide levels might increase the rate of growth of agricultural crops and forests, despite hotter temperatures and decreased soil moisture. Field trials have shown that if carbon dioxide levels increase to 550 parts per million (from today's 411 parts per million), the yields for rice, wheat and soybean crops will increase by nearly 15 per cent (although there is no measurable difference in the yields for maize and sorghum). While this is a good outcome, the increased yields are small and provide inadequate compensation for the storms, sea-level rises and other afflictions of climate change.

In addition, the changes induced in plants by elevated temperatures and carbon dioxide levels might include some nasty side effects. In some plants, the balance between protein and carbohydrates will be affected, as well as the production of naturally occurring toxins that deter pests and diseases. Early work on sugar gums and clover showed that when grown under carbon dioxide levels approximately double that of today, the proportion of cyanide-releasing chemicals increases relative to protein. Equivalent studies are yet to be performed in food crops, but there is cause for concern. For example, cassava is the staple crop of more than 500 million people, mostly in Africa. Cassava has to be carefully prepared to eliminate or substantially reduce its naturally occurring cyanide. Even so, 9 per cent of people in Nigeria suffer from some degree of cyanide poisoning. If the proportion of naturally occurring cyanide in cassava were to increase because of elevated carbon dioxide levels, the consequences could be severe.

We will never reduce our impact on the planet to pre-industrial levels, but how the anthropogenic era unfolds will depend on how we coexist with our planet despite the pressure exerted by our overwhelming numbers. We can postpone action and live with climate extremes, or we can minimise our impact on the planet and enjoy a stable climate. The choice is ours.

Global warming is among many environmental problems that must be solved, including water shortages, toxic waste management, biodiversity loss, plastic waste and resource depletion. But global warming is in many ways the most wicked. It has the broadest impact, affecting every part of the planet. Its causes are numerous, delayed, cumulative and occurring in every country. Fixes require global action. Solutions are massively expensive and require behavioural change. Global solutions sometimes require sacrifices at the local level.

While there is an understandable tendency to focus on temperature targets, or the climate itself, these are both lagging indicators. That is, they are the result of greenhouse gas emissions. The leading indicator, and the one we can directly control, is the emissions themselves.

Before we go any further, a word on the meaning of "zero." The term is something of a conundrum in the world of energy and emissions. In the main, I think it means "low" or "very low," so in general I will use low emissions and zero emissions to mean the same thing. I'm reluctant to be specific, but if I were stood against a wall with a gun pointed at my head, I would say that "low" means less than 10 per cent of where we started. That would be very good compared with where we are now.

The task ahead is, quite simply, immense. We cannot abruptly cease our use of energy. It is an essential pillar of our civilisation. Imagine a world without medicine: back to the Renaissance. Imagine a world without formal education: back to the Middle Ages. Imagine a world without dispatchable energy: back to the Stone Age.

Civilisation depends on taming and using energy. Our modern technology-heavy economy consumes vast amounts of it, mostly from coal, oil and natural gas. Globally, burning fossil fuels contributes nearly three-quarters of humanity's greenhouse gas emissions.

In 2003, Richard Smalley, the 1996 Nobel Prize laureate for Chemistry, ranked energy at the top of his list of ten major problems to be solved in the first half of the century, as the global population swells to near 10 billion people. As he pointed out, once we find a source of plentiful and clean energy, we can find solutions to the other pressing problems, including paths to sufficient food and water, and alleviating poverty. Smalley also made the observation that if we could all agree on the biggest problem, we would be well on the way to solving it.

On a side note, just as Smalley's vision drove my understanding of the importance of energy, architect Buckminster Fuller's vision quoted on the first page of this essay helped me understand the transformational role of breakthrough innovation. Although I came across Smalley and Fuller while investigating separate issues, there is a fitting connection. Richard Smalley's Nobel Prize was for the discovery of a new form of carbon in which sixty carbon atoms form a spherical structure, like a soccer ball and like the geodesic dome invented by Fuller. Smalley and his colleagues named the newly discovered carbon molecule buckminster-fullerene, in honour of Buckminster Fuller.

Smalley's perspective on the importance of energy was also held by Nikola Tesla, as compellingly depicted in the movie *The Current War*. Competing with George Westinghouse to bring electricity to the cities of

America, Tesla describes energy glowingly as being "as fundamental as food, as water, as air," and insists, "you cannot say that only those with money can eat, or can breathe."

Now, as huge swathes of humanity emerge from poverty to enter the middle class, the demand for energy and goods continues to rise. And so do emissions. Slowing or reversing the progress of billions of people out of poverty is not acceptable. Depopulating the cities and encouraging residents to adopt a frugal lifestyle in the country is not practicable. Cutting global population growth and even reversing it has often been suggested, but never enacted. Cutting consumption of goods and services, reducing air travel and eliminating red meat from our diets are often discussed, but rarely adopted.

In some cases, we are even going in the wrong direction. For example, consumers worldwide are increasingly purchasing large SUVs instead of sedans. As a result, fuel economy for passenger vehicles is getting worse, instead of better. And worldwide, usage of air conditioning keeps increasing, requiring ever more electricity to be generated.

Adding to the complexity of the task, the balance between preserving local environments and minimising global impact is often skewed in favour of the local, with a net harmful effect. For example, if global warming reaches 3°C above the pre-industrial baseline, it has been estimated that 8.5 per cent of known species will become extinct, which equates to the loss of approximately 100,000 species. So, if flooding a valley to build a hydroelectric dam that allows us to close several coal-fired power stations displaces local animals and plants, is that a trade-off that we should favourably consider? These are the choices that global warming forces on us – and will do so more and more.

The challenges of switching the world to clean energy are almost beyond comprehension. The energy and industrial systems contribute tens of trillions of dollars to the global economy every year.

There is no time to waste. This is not because the ravages of climate change lie at the bottom of a tall cliff and things suddenly go from tolerable to disastrous in a particular year. Rather, the problems become worse for each fraction of a degree change. We must move as fast and hard as is practicable to prevent the accumulation of detrimental impacts. But we have to be realistic. I often see graphs that show a steady rise in emissions to the current year, then a point of inflection and a downward slope projected for future years. This is not realistic, as evidenced by the appearance of a similar graph the following year, showing the same kind of projection, except the point of inflection and downward slope has shifted forward one year. The notion that we can suddenly reverse the slope of emissions is implausible. The reversal will take time, because the global energy systems, industry, agriculture and everything else our civilisation depends on are immense and cannot turn on a dime.

Humanity has undergone transitions at this scale before, but they were always driven by immediate benefits. The transition from people power to animal power meant that farmers could plough large fields and couriers could get from A to B much faster. The transition from horse power to steam power opened up previously unimagined industrial opportunities and led to mass transport. The transition from coal-fired steam engines to diesel engines for trains cut the expense and the plumes of black smoke. The transition from town gas to natural gas allowed us to heat our buildings and run our factories at lower cost and with greater safety.

In contrast, till recently there were no immediate performance or economic benefits in replacing fossil-fuel electricity with solar and wind. The latter are variable sources of energy that generate when they want rather than when the load demands; they do not intrinsically have the robust voltage and frequency performance of the fossil-fuel generators; they were not even remotely cost-competitive when they were introduced. The transition to solar and wind electricity did not commence because of the immediate benefits; it was driven by the external need to protect us from climate change.

It is, however, flawed thinking and a failure of ambition to imagine that this shift must be accompanied by a hit to our economy. Former Japanese prime minister Shinzō Abe described his country's ambition as accelerating

"the virtuous cycle of environmental protection and economic growth."
He did not say "or"; he said "and."

The Australian government's Low Emissions Technology Statement,
released in September 2020 by the Minister for Energy and Emissions
Reduction, Angus Taylor, outlines a vision for "a prosperous Australia, recognised as a global low emissions technology leader." Again, no trade-off,
no dichotomy. Prosperity *and* low emissions. It is my firm belief we can
have both. A December 2020 analysis by McKinsey & Company showed
that for Europe, a net-zero target can be achieved by 2050 at net-zero cost,
and with a net gain of 5 million jobs across the European economy.

The good news is that there is momentum. From 2005 to 2018, the
OECD countries cut emissions by an average of 9 per cent, Australia by
13 per cent. This decline is despite an increase in population and an
increase in exports.

In Australia, there is increasing action and ambition at state and federal
levels. At the federal level, we've had the Renewable Energy Target (RET)
attract solar and wind generation into the system, the Australian Renewable
Energy Agency (ARENA) and the Clean Energy Finance Corporation (CEFC)
assist industry with demonstration projects and large-scale deployment, and
the Emissions Reduction Fund (ERF) draw down carbon dioxide in the
atmosphere through biosequestration and other means. In recent years,
we've had the reform of the National Electricity Market (NEM), the National
Hydrogen Strategy and the Low Emissions Technology Investment Roadmap.

All of the states and territories have committed to net-zero emissions by
2050. Nationally, the Australian government commitment is for a 26 to
28 per cent cut in emissions by 2030. Given the projected population
growth from 20 million people in 2005 to 30 million in 2030, the lower
limit of 26 per cent represents a 50 per cent reduction per capita.

In November 2020, New South Wales legislated the construction of 12 gigawatts of solar and wind electricity in three renewable energy zones. The
legislation also included two gigawatts of storage, some of which will be for
up to eight hours. All new electricity generation in New South Wales will be

centrally planned. Support will be through contracts that provide certainty on minimum price and share the risk between government and investor.

The ACT has used such contracts for several years to support the construction of new solar and wind farms in New South Wales and other states that will produce at least as much as the ACT's annual electricity needs. Batteries are not required in this instance, because, like Denmark, the ACT has strong electrical interconnections to other, much bigger electricity regions.

In late 2020, the South Australian government confirmed its intention to reduce greenhouse gas emissions by more than 50 per cent by 2030, and in December announced an Electric Vehicle Action Plan to create a state-wide fast-charging network, shift the state government vehicle fleet to electric vehicles, and encourage local government and corporate fleets to do the same.

The Victorian government introduced incentives for householders to replace old heaters with modern heat-pump systems and install home solar and battery systems. Victoria has a target of 50 per cent renewable electricity by 2030 and has already met its interim target of 25 per cent by 2020. The Victorian government is funding six renewable energy zones.

In November 2020, the Tasmanian premier, Guy Barnett, announced that the state's electricity system has sufficient capacity to provide 100 per cent renewable electricity. Tasmania's plan is to double renewable electricity generation by 2040, with the surplus being used for clean-energy sales, either as hydrogen or ammonia for export, or as electricity sent by cable to the mainland.

Queensland has a target to cut emissions by 30 per cent by 2030 from the 2005 level. However, there is some concern about meeting this target because between 2006 and 2018 emissions went up 7 per cent, an increase attributed to the coal-seam gas boom. To reach the target, the government established a $500 million Renewable Energy Fund in 2020, and in November, in an Australian first, it created a ministry for hydrogen.

For its part, Western Australia is investing strongly in renewable hydrogen.

The ambition and commitment of state and territory governments is contributing greatly to the momentum across the country. However, these unilateral decisions are also putting the commercial operation of the National Electricity Market under severe strain, because interventions by government tend to require subsequent interventions to balance the prior interventions, ultimately leading to more centralised control rather than economically efficient markets.

On the other hand, it can be argued that during times of large and incredibly rapid technological change, no market design can keep up. State and territory governments justify their intervention on the basis that electricity is an essential service and shortages are unacceptable. That is, some things are too important to be left to the free market. America would never have landed a person on the Moon if it had relied on private enterprise. The new central planning approach in New South Wales, for example, is in part to deliver lower-emissions electricity, but also deals with the looming shortage from the closure of four out of the state's five big coal-fired electricity stations between now and 2035. These five power stations currently generate 80 per cent of New South Wales's electricity. They also contribute 36 per cent of the state's greenhouse gas emissions.

It is not easy to judge whether a national approach to the electricity market is better or worse than independent management within state and territory borders. But what is a no-brainer is that the physical operation of the electricity network spanning six jurisdictions must remain centrally controlled. This is because, from an electron's point of view, state borders are irrelevant. Electrons always seek to flow down the path of least resistance, and if that takes them across a state border, so be it. Plus, a failure in one state can cause problems in neighbouring states. Managing this single, joined-up physical network is the job of the Australian Energy Market Operator (AEMO), and it does its job very well.

Long-distance interconnectors should also be planned on a national basis, because each of them affects the operation of the whole multi-state network. They can be used to shift solar and wind electricity thousands of kilometres from areas of high output to areas of high demand. The limitations are cost, construction time and coincident weather patterns that sometimes cover areas as large as half of Australia. The new national approach to interconnector planning, known as the Integrated System Plan (ISP), is even more important as states and territories go it alone within their borders, because otherwise interstate interconnectors will be subject to the unsurprising inclination of each state to act as an exporter, not an importer.

Overall, we are moving inexorably towards a low-emissions future, albeit mainly in the electricity sector, rather than, say, transport. There is momentum also among industry and investors. Corporations are now major drivers of investment in renewable electricity. Since 2017, they have signed more than half of the power-purchase agreements with new solar and wind farms.

Most of our largest superannuation funds, businesses and groups such as the Business Council of Australia back the adoption of a 2050 target. Globally, there are new supersized clean-energy companies emerging, such as Enel, Iberdrola, NextEra Energy, Ørsted and China Energy Investment. They are not household names, but they are valued in the tens of billions of dollars. In October 2020, the market capitalisation of Florida-based NextEra briefly exceeded that of ExxonMobil.

Internationally, there are strong commitments from many countries. The United Kingdom is at the forefront, having reduced emissions by 34 per cent from 2005 to 2018, and through its upcoming role as host of the twenty-sixth UN climate conference in Glasgow in November this year. In June 2019, the UK became the first major economy to adopt a legally binding obligation to reach net-zero emissions by 2050, and it has now released a Ten Point Plan to get there. Some elements of the plan would be highly contentious in Australia, such as "delivering new and advanced nuclear power." Others, such as "accelerating the shift to zero emission vehicles," have a long way to go.

Germany, Denmark and many other European countries have strong targets to cut emissions, although some are finding that it is slow going.

And now there is a sea change pending for the United States. The linchpin of the Biden administration plan is a US$2 trillion investment over the next four years to set the country on its way to zero-emissions electricity supply by 2035. On his first day in office, President Biden signed an order for the United States to re-join the Paris Agreement. A week later, he signed orders "putting the climate crisis at the centre of United States foreign policy and national security" and committing all government agencies to contribute to a government-wide approach. He will also host a leaders' climate summit on 22 April, with the intention to raise international climate ambition. The pace of change is breathtaking.

As we track emissions from individual nations, we should note that in many advanced countries, emissions are falling partly because their heavily emitting domestic industries have shifted to emerging countries, and the advanced countries now import a large fraction of the manufactured goods they consume. This does nothing, of course, to reduce global emissions. The standard way to count emissions is to measure them within borders, which makes sense, because when all countries' emissions are added up, this gives the global total. While there would be some logic in attributing emissions according to where goods are consumed rather than manufactured, it would be difficult to do so accurately, and would completely undermine the continuity of our historical records. A further quirk is that international aviation and shipping are currently not attributed to any country; instead, they are estimated and reported separately.

While we recognise climate change as a global phenomenon and the solutions as global, we must also acknowledge that inaction by one country does not justify inaction by another. This goes well beyond the fundamental ethical argument of doing the right thing. At one Senate Estimates committee hearing, I was quizzed about Australia's small contribution to global emissions. Australia is responsible for about 1.3 per cent of emissions, and I was pressed on what impact it would have on climate change if we eliminated our share. I had to agree with the supposition put to me that a 1.3 per cent reduction would have virtually no impact in and of itself. But, as I said then, if each voter took that approach at election time, we would not have a democracy. A single vote makes no difference. But every vote counts. Just as every tonne of emissions counts. How many of us would make a serious argument not to recycle our household cans, plastics and bottles on the basis that what one household recycles can make no difference to the global effort? Momentum builds one brick at a time.

So there is an ethical argument and there is a logical argument. There is also an economic argument. In the end, momentum will sweep the globe, and it won't matter whether any single country is in the driver's seat, in the passenger's seat, or on rollerskates holding a tow rope. At least, it won't matter in a global sense. It will, though, certainly make a difference to the wealth of individual countries such as Australia whether they are in the lead or jostling with the hangers-on or mingling with the coalition of the unwilling. All countries will eventually participate, if not because they see the light, then as a result of consumer or diplomatic pressure, and possibly because they will face trade tariffs to adjust for otherwise untaxed carbon in what they export. In Australia's case, demand for coal, oil and natural gas exports will diminish, irrespective of what we do. This is because our major trading partners, such as Japan, South Korea, China, the United Kingdom and the United States, have declared their ambition to make the shift to clean energy. So too have individual companies. For example, South Korean steel manufacturer POSCO has pledged that its operations will be carbon-neutral by 2050, using transformational technologies relying on hydrogen, instead of coal, in steel-making. It is essential, from an economic viewpoint, that we invest now to develop alternative energy exports.

Within Australia, some will be motivated by wanting to protect the climate. Others will be persuaded by the economic realities and opportunities. Others by the sheer exhilaration of investing in new technology. When Senator Matt Canavan expressed to me his support for a national hydrogen strategy, his hope may have been that Australia will become a major exporter of this commodity, irrespective of why the world adopts it. The point is that there are many reasons to invest in the low-emissions technology transition, all leading to the desired outcome of reducing emissions of greenhouse gases into the atmosphere.

Shortly after releasing our review of the National Electricity Market in 2017, I appeared on the ABC's *Q&A*, where I joined a panel alongside energy minister Josh Frydenberg, shadow energy minister Mark Butler, the Climate Council's Amanda McKenzie and the CEO of Energy Consumers Australia, Rosemary Sinclair. In the audience were some of the 750 Hazelwood power station employees who lost their jobs when the La Trobe Valley coal-fired plant closed that year. Audience members asked questions as wide-ranging as how to manage the job losses and community impact when large coal-fired power stations close down, why electricity prices were increasing, and what chance Australia had of meeting its Paris climate targets. We were a microcosm of the debate; all that was missing was a Russian oil oligarch and Elon Musk.

In response to a question from host Tony Jones, I described myself as possibly the only genuinely technology-neutral person in the room. Then, as now, I argued to elevate the debate away from an argument about a temperature target, and away from a debate about renewables versus coal, to the question of overall emissions. As I said then, if the right mix of existing coal and renewables gives you the trajectory to cut emissions that you want, that is the best path to follow.

In my view, progress is hampered by some at one end of the debate who want no change at all, and others at the other end who want to move faster than is feasible. The slow transition camp comprises the people who prefer things to stay the same or change slowly. They're nervous about the economic impact, they're concerned about the effort, or they don't want to admit they were wrong. No matter the reason, their sluggishness is such that if they prevail globally, we will be doomed to a dangerously warmer planet. If they prevail in Australia, we will suffer economically from not developing the cheapest form of electricity, and potentially from trade restrictions imposed by other countries that are determined to decarbonise.

The fast transition camp comprises those who want to shift the world to a zero-emissions economy fast, very fast. However, it is simply unrealistic to think that with political will we can immediately reverse course. This does not sufficiently acknowledge that the overall energy system is huge, and changing it is indescribably more difficult than putting solar panels on rooftops or providing subsidies for electric cars. In their pursuit of perfection, they deny the implementers the tools that would enable emissions to be rapidly reduced, albeit not quite to zero.

Those in the slow transition camp want to build more of their favourite technology – coal generators – because they worked well in the past, so why shouldn't we have more of the same; and because they want to preserve the jobs of the past rather than deal with the adjustments required to capitalise on the jobs of the future.

Those in the fast transition camp advocate the immediate shutdown of coal despite the economic calamity this would cause, and deny the use of natural gas to support the fastest possible massive adoption of solar and wind electricity. We are also asked to accomplish this task without using zero-emissions nuclear, new catchment hydroelectricity or hydrogen from fossil fuels with carbon capture and permanent storage. This litany of proscribed approaches does not make the task impossible, but it certainly makes it more difficult.

Before I became Australia's chief scientist, I co-founded G Magazine, a green lifestyle magazine. I had invested early in low-emissions technology stocks and was chief technology officer for Better Place Australia, a company that planned a network of electric car battery-swapping stations. My wife and I have two electric cars and we pay a premium for renewable electricity at our home in Melbourne. So I am enthusiastic about the net-zero revolution, but I reject any evangelical commitment to one source of energy over another, because my overarching interest is to use the best tools possible to limit emissions to slow down global warming.

We can all agree that low or near-zero emissions is the endgame. There is more than one way to get there, and I believe that we will get there more easily if we disentangle ourselves from the technologies to which we are attached and keep our eye on the aim.

My approach stems partly from my background as an engineer. In engineering, the first step in developing a solution is to identify the problem, which might sound trite, but it is a step too often skipped. The problem we must fix in this case is the anthropogenic emission of carbon dioxide and other greenhouse gases into the atmosphere. That's the outcome that counts. Not the percentage of renewables. That is an operational metric. Not the amount of hydrogen produced. That is an operational metric. Not the number of coal-fired stations in use. That, too, is an operational metric.

So, yes, for me technology agnosticism includes coal. If the technology becomes feasible and economically viable to capture the carbon dioxide produced by coal-fired power plants and store it permanently underground so that coal can be burnt without contributing to greenhouse gases, then why not, as I said to the ABC audience. In reality, it is unlikely that the economics will ever make that possible, but more on that later.

My interest is in the future of our planet and its life. Astronomical surveys of the stars in our Milky Way galaxy have found thousands of exoplanets, and so far what those surveys are telling us, along with surveys of the planets in our own solar system, is that Earth's ability to sustain life is unique. The reverberations of that thought are reason enough for action.

I always admired the laconic phrase "Houston, we have a problem," as used in the 1995 movie *Apollo 13* to presage a huge issue that will require the undivided attention of the ground-based experts and the astronauts. The objective was clear: complete the mission without injury or loss of life. When it comes to climate change, you could say, "Houston, we have a problem." The objective is clear: change civilisation's practices so that we preserve our climate.

How do we change the practices of our civilisation? We make a plan. The plan must recognise the realities – of scale, difficulty and uncertainty. The plan must be ambitious but not naive, must start by acknowledging how difficult decarbonisation will be, and must keep costs for the consumer as low as possible and ensure service remains reliable. The plan must focus on large-scale technology and policy solutions.

Technology does not live in a vacuum. It lives in a policy-driven world of markets, fiscal settings, taxes, government decisions and consumer preferences. This essay is about the technology, not the policies, which are for our democratically elected political leaders to determine. Governments have to balance competing priorities across economic growth, scientific advice and community values. Pursuing economic growth as the only priority would have environmental consequences; pursuing emissions reduction as the only priority would have economic consequences. But the overriding goal of our national plan must be to lower emissions across the whole of the economy.

To this end, we need market designs that support the adoption of low-emissions technologies. We need incentives that encourage investors. We need stretch goals to motivate industry and calibrate performance.

We have combined regulations, technology and ingenuity to great advantage, again and again. Consider cars. In the 1920s, there were 240 vehicle fatalities per billion miles driven in America. It would have been tempting to ban cars! Instead, over many decades, we worked at the problem with a combination of regulations and technology. Regulations include speed limits and severe punishments for drink driving. Technology includes airbags, seatbelts and crumple zones. Today, the fatality rate is down to 12 per billion miles, a mere 5 per cent of the high point.

Or consider pollutants. Until the 1950s, automobiles and trucks released ever-increasing amounts of toxic pollutants, such as nitrogen oxides and sulphur dioxide. Then, in 1959, California introduced novel legislation to force car manufacturers to clean up their act. Facing a series of ever tougher legal requirements, automobile manufacturers developed catalytic converters, engine management computers and fuel injection systems that perform so well that nowadays, according to some manufacturers, the exhaust fumes from their cars are cleaner than the inlet air sucked into the engine. Just as technology got us into trouble through its propensity to generate carbon dioxide emissions, it is technology that will save us.

However, even a very good plan needs a measure of good luck and good timing. Consider the experience of Germany, a leader in renewable energy. Its *Energiewende*, or "energy transition plan," was launched in 2000. In the nineteen years that followed, the share of primary energy derived from fossil fuels fell from approximately 84 per cent to 78 per cent. In the United States, both ambition and planning have fallen well short of Germany, but the share of primary energy from fossil fuels fell about the same amount over the period, from 86 per cent to 80 per cent. In Australia, because we have no nuclear power, our starting position is much higher. The share of primary energy derived from fossil fuels fell from approximately 96 per cent to 91 per cent. But these numbers do not tell the whole story. The remarkable thing about Germany's commitment is that its investment helped to forge the global solar and wind industries and underwrite falling prices.

The best way to deliver planned obsolescence in the energy sector quickly is by an adaptive approach – that is, an approach that can adapt as technologies evolve and prices reduce. Time and again, the renewable technology industry has delivered new capabilities and lower prices ahead of expectation. We need to target technologies for investment – as is done in the Low Emissions Technology Statement – but we need to be prepared to shift as technologies shift; thus, the need for annual reviews.

Which brings me to a much-debated issue. Australia is under increasing pressure to set a date for net-zero emissions. The majority of countries, and very many states, territories, companies and investors, have committed to a net-zero target by 2050 or 2060. Some, like the United Kingdom, have articulated a clear pathway. However, not all have a plan for how to get there, and in some cases sectors of the economy have been excluded. For example, New

Zealand does not fully include methane emissions from agriculture and waste, which contribute about half of its emissions. In other places, the target has not yet manifested itself in the necessary investments. For example, China has announced a 2060 net-zero target, but on current plans it will build up to 200 gigawatts of new coal generation between now and 2025, balanced in part by an intention to close down small and inefficient coal plants.

In Australia, Prime Minister Scott Morrison has said that "our goal is to reach net-zero emissions as soon as possible, and preferably by 2050" and that getting to zero "is no longer about if or when, but importantly, how."

So, let's get started

It begins with electrons. They spend eternity darting around in a frenzy, never stopping, never tiring, never ageing. They are so tiny that the most powerful microscope in the world cannot see them. It takes huge numbers of them to have an impact. They have underpinned my career and they have profoundly influenced the existence of all of us.

When they work together, electrons create electricity. To heat one litre of water in an electric kettle, approximately 60 billion billion electrons must flow through the kettle every second. In the ten minutes it takes to boil the water, 36,000 billion billion electrons will each have contributed a tiny amount of effort to heat the water for your tea or coffee. An industrious, well-behaved, predictable army.

The taming of electricity was arguably the most significant technological advance in the history of humankind. The rapid developments from the year 1800, when Alessandro Volta invented the first electric battery, have been astonishing. Electricity is everywhere. Without it our world would be bereft of kettles, street lighting, cars, trains, refrigerators, washing machines, televisions, computers, phones and the internet.

My personal fascination has been life-long. For me, electricity is a tool, a colleague, a friend and an opportunity. As a young boy, I played with crystal radios; as a youth, I made digital clocks. As a neuroscientist, I designed equipment to measure the electrical activity of brain cells. The electrical activity in brain cells is exquisitely small. The current is measured in nanoamps (a billionth of an amp) and the voltage is measured in millivolts (a thousandth of a volt). For the technically inclined, this means that at the level of a single brain cell the power is in picowatts (a millionth of a millionth of a watt).

Later in my career, I worked at a company specifying and implementing charge stations for electric cars. There, the currents are in the tens of amps, the voltages are in the hundreds and the power is in the thousands of watts (kilowatts).

Then, quite suddenly, in late 2016, my world of electricity scaled up, big time. On 28 September 2016, South Australia was hit by a series of storms, accompanied by micro-tornadoes, that toppled steel pylons holding up long-distance transmission lines. Fault currents surged and coursed through other parts of the network, causing the interconnector between Victoria and South Australia to close down to save itself. This resulted in more fault currents, and ultimately the disconnection of a number of wind farms that were exposed to the surges. Then, as the fault currents rippled through the system, the South Australian network collapsed and the state was in blackout.

A week later I got a call from the then energy minister, Josh Frydenberg, to ask me to chair a review of the National Electricity Market. At once, I had to think in thousands of amps, hundreds of thousands of volts, and billions of watts (gigawatts). Fortunately, the physics of electricity scales linearly, so I was able to apply my training in microelectronics and brain cell electrophysiology to electricity grids. Since then, my focus has expanded to energy in all of its facets, but electricity remains at the heart of it.

Australia's emissions profile

Figure 4 shows, in Australia in 2020, our greenhouse gas emissions across major sectors. Total emissions were 513 million tonnes, down nearly 17 per cent from 2005 and 3 per cent from 2019. This significant reduction last year is attributable to COVID-19 restrictions that reduced traffic of all kinds, the increased penetration of renewable electricity, and some effect of drought on agricultural emissions.

Figure 4: *Sectoral breakdown of 2020 emissions in Australia in millions of tonnes of carbon dioxide equivalent*

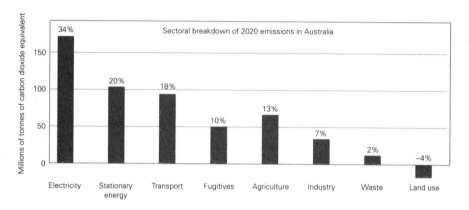

Source: Data from Australia's emissions projections 2020, published December 2020, table 2.

The definition of what is included in each sector is important:

Electricity   Emissions from the combustion of fuels to generate electricity.

Stationary energy   Emissions from the combustion of fuels to generate steam, heat or pressure, other than for electricity generation and transport.

Transport   Emissions from the combustion of fuels for transportation within Australia.

Fugitives   Emissions released during the extraction, processing and delivery of fossil fuels.

Agriculture   Emissions from livestock, manure management and crop residue, emissions from rice cultivation, application of nitrogen to soils, and burning of agricultural residues.

Industry   Emissions from non-energy-related industrial production and processes. Includes emissions from hydrofluorocarbons (HFCs) used in refrigerants and air conditioning.

| **Waste** | Emissions from the disposal of solid waste and wastewater. |

| **Land use** | Emissions and sequestration from activities occurring on forest lands, forests converted to other land uses, grasslands, croplands, wetlands and settlements. |

This division into eight sectors provides a useful way to consider the optimal path forward. Electricity, stationary energy and transport together account for 72 per cent of Australia's emissions – electricity 34 per cent, stationary energy 20 per cent, transport 18 per cent. Those emissions are from burning fossil fuels. In these sectors, to a very large extent the combustion of coal, oil and natural gas can be replaced by renewable electricity and clean hydrogen.

Fugitive emissions, accounting for nearly 10 per cent of Australia's emissions, are generated during fossil-fuel extraction and processing. In the near and medium term, we need to minimise fugitive emissions through practices such as carbon capture and permanent storage at the wellhead, but in the long term fugitives will go away by themselves, once fossil fuels are globally replaced in electricity generation, stationary energy and transport.

By tackling these fossil-fuel sectors, we can eliminate 82 per cent of greenhouse gas emissions and achieve what I refer to as the Electric Planet, in which instead of burning fossil fuels, all our primary energy is produced from zero-emissions electricity sources. This will be challenging, but the pathway is clear. After that, it gets difficult. The remaining emissions from agriculture (13 per cent), industry (7 per cent), waste (2 per cent) and land use (−4 per cent) need more research, testing and gradual change.

I will discuss solutions to the different sectors in turn, but in a few sentences it goes like this. Step 1: Replace all the existing electricity generation with zero-emissions electricity. Step 2: Generate lots more zero-emissions electricity, so that we can use it for stationary energy and transport. Step 3: Generate lots more electricity, so that we can use it to make hydrogen for those instances where electrons are not ideal and a high-density molecular fuel is needed, or to replace natural gas and coal in some cases as a chemical feedstock for industry. Step 4: For Australia, generate many times more electricity, to produce hydrogen for export. Step 5: Produce lots more electricity, to produce goods that embody large amounts of energy, such as zero-emissions steel and zero-emissions aluminium. All these steps can happen in parallel.

Non-starters

When faced with a huge challenge, we should stock our armamentarium with all the tools at our disposal and go into battle with both hands at the ready, but many of the clean electricity generation methods are denied to us, or are incapable of making a significant contribution.

Uranium and plutonium nuclear fission power stations produce electricity and heat at massive scale and do not emit any carbon dioxide. However, populations around the world live in fear of nuclear disaster — even though the actual safety record for nuclear electricity shows that it is one of the safest energy technologies ever developed. Rejection is further exacerbated by the nearly universal failure of national governments to show leadership in solving the problem of permanent nuclear waste disposal. In addition, the cost of electricity from new conventional nuclear reactors is high, too high to compete with solar and wind supported by batteries. There is a chance that a new style of nuclear reactor called a small modular reactor (SMR) might overcome the issues plaguing conventional nuclear reactors, but the first approved SMR will not be built in the United States till the end of this decade, which would push any conceivable adoption in Australia into the following decade.

Other forms of nuclear energy, such as hydrogen fusion and thorium fission, are under development, but despite decades of effort they are still far from being proven at demonstration scale, let alone commercial scale. So if they are able to contribute commercially, it will not be in the next two decades.

Large hydroelectric dams can produce zero-emissions electricity at massive scale. That's good for the planet, but new dams are routinely opposed by local communities because they flood valleys, affect the surrounding flora and fauna, and need transmission lines crossing forests to connect them to the electricity grid. In Australia, we have not built a large hydroelectric dam for more than fifty years.

Biomass, such as wood, can be burnt to produce electricity and it was the fuel for 2 per cent of global electricity production in 2018. Further, biomass such as algae or sugarcane can be converted to a liquid fuel alternative to petrol and diesel. However, if the biomass is grown especially for energy use, there are emissions associated with farming, and there is pressure on the use of agricultural land for food and the retention of native forests. It is simply not practical to replace a substantial fraction of our fossil-fuel use in this way. Bioenergy in Australia has only slightly increased since 2010, sitting at less than 1 per cent of our total energy production. Nevertheless, in extreme cases such as long-distance aviation, biofuels might contribute to the solution.

Waste to electricity is an important means of reducing methane emissions from decomposing matter. However, even when optimised, this process will only contribute a small portion of our electricity and heat needs.

At tiny scale, natural geothermal heat to produce electricity has been effective in Iceland, the west coast of the United States, and New Zealand, but it is in short supply elsewhere and all up contributed just 0.35 per cent of global electricity production in 2018.

Wave power and tidal power combined contributed a mere 0.005 per cent of global electricity production in 2018 despite decades of effort. Hot rock geothermal, also known as enhanced geothermal, has not reached commercial production. These are the also-rans of clean electricity generation.

Finally, exotic ideas such as giant mirrors and solar panels in space beaming energy as radio waves down to receivers on the ground are in the realm of science fiction and very likely to stay that way.

Solar and wind: the backbone

That leaves two obvious large-scale, zero-emissions sources of electrical energy: solar and wind. In the past twenty years, we have seen significant amounts of new solar photovoltaic and wind electricity added to the grid.

Solar photovoltaic is the more technical term for solar panels. Each panel contains many crystalline silicon sheets known as cells. These can be monocrystalline or polycrystalline cells, with the latter being less efficient in converting sunlight to electricity but lower in cost. There are no moving parts and the reliability is very high. The same kinds of panels are used for domestic rooftop installations as for giant solar farms; it is just that more of them are used in the latter.

Wind-generated electricity has also converged on a single approach. It turns out that the wind is stronger and more predictable high above the ground, so wind turbines, like giant mountain ash trees seeking the sunlight above the forest canopy, have grown taller over the years. And a bonus of the turbine being so high is that the blades can be longer and capture wind energy more efficiently.

As well as converging on big and tall, for many years now wind turbines have converged on a three-blade design. Why not dozens, like the old windmills that pump water for cattle on outback farms? Because each blade creates drag and reduces efficiency, so fewer is better. So why not one or two blades? Because with only one or two blades, there is insufficient balance, and thus a lot of vibration and stress on the tower. Three blades is the optimum number.

Modern wind turbines are massive. The biggest of the offshore turbines are around 10 megawatts capacity, with 13 megawatt monsters in the prototype phase. The largest onshore turbines are about 5 megawatts, standing 150 metres tall, with blades nearly 70 metres long and weighing 20 tonnes each.

At the time of the South Australian blackout in 2016, many people blamed renewables. But the true problem was not the renewables; it was the connection rules and the operational management of the electricity system.

Conventional generators fall into a category known as "synchronous," whereas solar and wind are in the "non-synchronous" category. Our electricity grid was designed for synchronous generators. The introduction of non-synchronous generators brings challenges that must be addressed.

In 1879, the streets of Melbourne were lit with gas lamps, but over at the Melbourne Cricket Ground the first night football match was played under electric arc lamps. The following year, the Victorian Electric Light Company was formed and the era of commercial electric operations began.

For the next 120 years, the principles of large-scale electricity generation were the same. Either coal, oil, natural gas or biomass were burnt and the heat was used to generate steam that shot through a turbine and turned a shaft. In the case of hydroelectricity, descending water from a dam powered a turbine to turn a shaft. More recently, solar thermal generators have entered operation. These concentrate sunlight onto a collector that becomes very hot. Through a heat exchanger, steam is created to drive a turbine and turn its shaft. In all cases, the shaft drives a generator configured to rotate at a constant speed and produce an alternating current (AC) and alternating voltage. The current and voltage alternate fifty times per second in Australia, sixty times per second in the United States.

In a system with dozens or hundreds of large generators connected by transmission lines, it is important that all the generators are synchronised so that their output currents and voltages alternate at exactly the same frequency; otherwise they will fight each other and the power system will collapse. With conventional generators, this is a well-understood and manageable task.

Another useful, intrinsic feature of these synchronous generators is that they have lots of rotational inertia because of their huge spinning mass. If there is a fault in the network that suddenly increases the load on the generators, within milliseconds they will enthusiastically increase their output without substantially changing frequency.

By contrast, solar photovoltaic and wind turbine generators are not intrinsically synchronous; therefore, they are not compatible with the synchronised operation of the existing electricity grid. Houston, we have a problem.

In the case of solar panels, the output does not alternate at all. Sophisticated electronic circuits called inverters turn the constant output into an appropriately alternating output at the required fifty cycles per second. In the case of wind, the output alternates but the frequency depends on the strength of the wind. Either mechanical controllers or electronic inverters are used to achieve an alternating output at fifty cycles per second. By these means, the frequency from solar and wind generators is maintained, but it takes a lot of attention and sometimes requires that special frequency maintenance devices such as synchronous condensers be added to the system.

The solar generators have no rotational inertia at all, and the wind generators do not have any useful inertia unless they are operated below their rated output. Again, sophisticated management of the interconnected network can overcome this limitation, and electronic circuits powered by batteries or banks of capacitors can synthesise the required inertia and frequency characteristics.

The problem in South Australia was National Electricity Market operation and design. The interconnector between Victoria and South Australia was operating too close to its limits given the storms, there were not enough conventional synchronous generators operating at the time, and the connection requirements for the wind farms had not been modernised to take into account their difference from conventional generators.

The overall point is that solar photovoltaic and wind generators are very different to traditional synchronous generators. Their virtue is that they don't produce any emissions. Their iniquity is that they don't help to maintain frequency control in the system. In the early days this was a huge concern, but as support devices have been developed to overcome the limitations and as the system operators have gained experience, it is now clear that it will be possible to achieve the ultimate goal of a zero-emissions electricity system.

The rate of installation of new solar and wind electricity is remarkable. In Australia, 99 per cent of all new electricity generation capacity in the past few years has been solar photovoltaic and wind. In the rest of the world, the comparable figure is a bit over half, because natural gas and coal-fired generators continue to be built. Approximately 30 per cent of suitable dwellings in Australia have solar rooftops, the highest proportion in the world.

By the end of 2019, on a per capita basis, solar capacity in Australia was the highest in the world, at 644 watts per person, ahead of Germany at 589 watts per person, Japan at 500 watts and Belgium at 425 watts. Because of our sunnier climate, the annual output from our solar panels in Australia is even further ahead.

The reason for this high rate of installation is a combination of the low cost of capital, the ever-falling price of solar panels and wind turbines, experience in deployment, demand from mining projects, the improved connection requirements managed by the Australian Energy Market Operator, the contracts and guarantees by state and territory governments, voluntary purchases by companies and local government, and the innovation and project appetite of Australian investors, developers and large-scale industrial and commercial customers. The Australian Renewable Energy Target (RET) was also very effective. In fact, it was so successful at bringing rooftop solar, large-scale solar and wind electricity generation into the market that it is no longer necessary.

But what does the overall picture look like? Annual electricity production for all of Australia is illustrated in Figure 5. "TWh" stands for terawatt-hours. Most of us are familiar with kilowatt-hours, because that is what we pay for on our electricity bill, at rates such as 25 cents per kilowatt-hour. Multiply by 1000 and you get megawatt-hours. Multiply by 1000 again for gigawatt-hours. Another 1000 and you have terawatt-hours.

In numbers, solar and wind electricity production in Australia in 2019 were 18 terawatt-hours and 20 terawatt-hours, respectively. That is 6.8 per

Figure 5: Annual electricity production by source

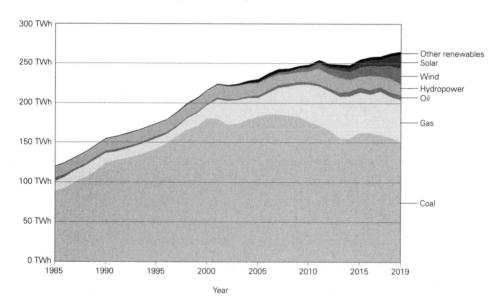

Source: *Our World in Data*, based on *BP Statistical Review of World Energy*.
Note: 'Other renewables' includes biomass and waste, geothermal, wave and tidal.

cent and 7.5 per cent of total electricity production. The combined total of 14.3 per cent is a substantial fraction, and good reason to be confident that the march towards 100 per cent renewable electricity is feasible.

Hydroelectricity was 14.3 terawatt-hours, or 5.4 per cent. Hydroelectricity production has been reasonably constant for more than thirty years and is unlikely to increase substantially in future.

To convert all of Australia's electricity supply to solar and wind, assuming no change to the contribution of hydroelectricity, we would have to increase the current solar and wind annual electricity production nearly sevenfold. Solar rooftops, large solar arrays and wind farms will generate the energy, supported by long-distance transmission lines, batteries, pumped hydro, hydrogen storage and smart software. The 21st-century power supply will be visible, but appropriately integrated into our expansive landscape.

The year 2018 was a banner one for renewable energy. Forbes Media reports this was the year the price of electricity from new-build solar and wind farms in the United States fell below the price of electricity from existing black coal generators. As Silvio Maracci wrote in *Forbes*, "It is now cheaper to save the climate than to destroy it."

Globally, the price of electricity from onshore wind farms fell 39 per cent in the past decade, and the average price of solar electricity per megawatt-hour plummeted by 82 per cent.

The cost of producing a megawatt-hour of solar and wind electricity from newly built plants in Australia is now in the vicinity of $50 and falling. Low levels of demand and high levels of generation of cheap solar and wind electricity saw the average price per megawatt-hour in the National Electricity Market in the last quarter of 2020 hovering in the mid $40s, well down on the average prices near $100 that prevailed in 2017. At an international seminar in December 2020, I heard from the CEO of a large Saudi Arabian company that the most recent prices for solar electricity were coming in at $17 per megawatt-hour and on track to reach $13 per megawatt-hour in a few years.

Even with costs of storage included, new solar outcompetes new fossil-fuel generation. For example, the Reserve Bank of Australia estimates that new solar in 2020 with six hours of pumped hydro storage would produce electricity for approximately $100 per megawatt-hour. And it will get cheaper every year. By contrast, because of higher performance expectations and the higher cost of finance, the price of new black coal-fired electricity has risen to an uncompetive price of approximately $150 per megawatt-hour. If a new coal-fired electricity generator were fitted with carbon capture and storage (CCS) to qualify as a high-efficiency, low-emissions (HELE) generator, the price has been estimated at more than $200 per megawatt-hour.

The financial risk of investing in a new coal-fired electricity plant is mirrored by the low valuation of current assets. For example, in December 2020, the two Japanese co-owners of the Bluewaters coal-fired electricity plant in Western Australia completely wrote off their $1.2 billion investment, despite it being the newest coal-fired electricity plant in Australia, built in 2009.

Capacity versus energy

When I projected a sevenfold increase in solar and wind, I was talking about generated output: that is, the amount of electrical energy produced each year. The amount of electrical energy that can be produced by a generator depends on its type. For example, if there is demand in the market, a 1-gigawatt coal-fired generator can produce much more electrical energy over the course of a year than a 1-gigawatt solar farm.

Let's look at some specifics. Allowing for maintenance, if there is sufficient customer demand, a coal-fired generator might operate at full power 90 per cent of the time. This fraction is known as the capacity factor. In reality, because of market conditions – fluctuating demand over time – it would be unlikely to operate at this theoretical level.

Maintenance on solar and wind generators is low, but they nevertheless can only operate for a fraction of the hours in a year. Take solar generation. It certainly does not work at night, it operates at reduced capacity during the mornings and evenings, it produces less if the sky is overcast and less again during short winter days. On average, over the course of a year, the capacity factor of a solar generator in a good location such as central Australia might be 25 per cent, or in a poor location such as south-eastern Australia 10 per cent. Wind generation, similarly, is subject to the vagaries of the wind. The capacity factor for wind generators varies from about 30 per cent to 50 per cent.

This means that a 1-gigawatt coal-fired generator can generate a lot more energy in a year than a 1-gigawatt solar or wind generator. This distinction is very important. It means that to replace the annual energy available from a coal-fired generator such as the 2-gigawatt Liddell power station scheduled to close in 2023, you need a lot more than 2 gigawatts of solar or wind generation capacity.

As a rule of thumb, to replace a 1-gigawatt coal generator that operates at, say, 60 per cent capacity factor requires:

- 1.2 gigawatts of wind generation at 50 per cent capacity factor

- 2 gigawatts of wind generation at 30 per cent capacity factor

- 2.4 gigawatts of solar generation at 25 per cent capacity factor

- 6 gigawatts of solar generation at 10 per cent capacity factor.

At the start of 2021, there was 23 gigawatts of coal-fired generation capacity in Australia. It is difficult to know how much solar and wind will be required to replace the existing output, because it will depend on the mix of solar and wind installed in future. Useful guidance comes from the central projection by the Australian Energy Market Operator, which shows that a 13 gigawatt decline in coal capacity over the next two decades would require a 34-gigawatt increase in solar and wind capacity.

Efficiency

There are two types of efficiency relevant to this discussion: production efficiency and usage efficiency. To start with production efficiency: because solar panels are made from silicon, it is easy to think that perhaps their efficiency will double every few years, in the same way that the performance of silicon integrated circuits used in computers regularly improves, according to the famous Moore's law. However, Moore's law is a measure of human ingenuity, not physics. It turns out to be impossible for basic silicon solar panels ever to double their efficiency again.

It used to be possible. In 1839, when French physicist Edmond Becquerel discovered the photovoltaic effect – a voltage created when some materials are exposed to light – the efficiency was unmeasurably low. Forty-four years later, American inventor Charles Fritts developed the first practical photovoltaic solar cell, with 1 per cent efficiency. Over the years, the efficiency doubled more than four times, and today's commercially available silicon solar cells operate at about 22 per cent efficiency.

In considering where the efficiency might reach, it is important to note that not all the energy of the sunlight is in colours that the solar panels can convert. It is widely estimated that the maximum theoretical conversion efficiency of silicon solar panels based on the spectrum of sunlight is about 33 per cent. Thus, silicon solar panel efficiency will never again double. But the cost of solar panels will continue to come down. And every time there is a small increase in efficiency, from say 22 per cent to 23 per cent, the rooftop or land area needing to be covered for the same electrical energy comes down proportionately.

Similarly for wind turbines. Most extract about 35 per cent to 45 per cent of the energy from the wind that passes through the swept area of the rotors, rising to 50 per cent in strong winds. The theoretical maximum is approximately 59 per cent, so there is no prospect of ever doubling the efficiency.

Let's consider now the second kind of efficiency, which is how the energy is used. Obviously, if our use of energy were more efficient, we would not have to produce nearly as much. Here, doublings can and have occurred, multiple times. For example, the best modern light-emitting diodes are so much more efficient than the old incandescent globes they replaced that it takes only about a tenth of the electricity to achieve the same room lighting level today as it did at the turn of the century.

A gigawatt of power that does not need to be generated is the best way to reduce emissions and costs. Insulating our buildings, installing modern appliances, using light-emitting diodes instead of incandescent lamps, and cutting waste in industrial processes all help to reduce the amount of energy used.

Enabling technologies

The upper limit of solar and wind installation in the Australian electricity market is determined to some extent by our ability to manage the millions of solar rooftop generators and by transmission capacity for large-scale solar and wind electricity.

Currently, a new rooftop solar system is added in Australia every six minutes. It has been suggested that in future, on some days, rooftop solar systems and batteries could supply between 20 per cent and 50 per cent of peak daytime demand. Managing all of these separate contributions to the electricity grid so that they assist with system operation and stability is known as distributed energy resource management.

Demand response management is a complementary approach, in which large industrial loads and smaller residential and commercial loads are instructed to delay or reduce their operation, which lowers the peak demand, and thus the needed capacity.

Operations at this level of sophistication require computational software for system modelling and operations, aggregation and management of solar rooftops and domestic batteries, control systems to manage distributed loads, two-way power flows and peer-to-peer sharing. All of these technologies are in their early stages, and as they develop they will contribute to reliable and affordable electricity. Aware of these opportunities, a Google affiliate named X is developing software systems to turbo-charge these enabling technologies. X recently recruited the CEO of the Australian Energy Market Operator, Audrey Zibelman, to lead this effort, to benefit from her experience introducing these capabilities into the Australian electricity market.

These enabling technologies are not themselves primary sources of energy. However, they are an important part of the march to low emissions because they help us integrate more solar and wind reliably and cost-effectively.

For large-scale solar and wind, an important advance is the Integrated System Plan (ISP). The plan will connect new Renewable Energy Zones (REZ) to the main electricity grid, and it has already documented the new long-distance interconnectors that will be required to bring electrons from where they are generated to where they are needed. The connection of Renewable Energy Zones was inspired by what we saw in Texas: the Competitive Renewable Energy Zones (CREZ) initiative that built transmission lines to the wind-rich zones in the west of Texas and the panhandle in the north-west, and ultimately supported the connection of 23 gigawatts of new wind electricity.

Combine the ISP with accurate weather forecasting, improved software for the grid operator, high levels of investment in large-scale solar and wind generators and long-distance transmission lines, and a pathway to producing all of our electricity from renewable sources becomes visible. The endpoint will be electricity that is cheap, zero-emissions and highly reliable.

But to get to a fully zero-emissions energy system – the Electric Planet – we need even more tools in our armamentarium. The naysayers are right: there will be times when the wind doesn't blow and the sun doesn't shine. It's a serious problem! As with most problems, there are solutions. Many solutions. These include building more generation capacity than our essential needs and using the excess when it is available for variable industrial processes, such as producing hydrogen; long-distance interconnectors, as discussed above, to bring electricity to the customer from where the wind is blowing and the sun is shining; storage of solar and wind electricity when more is being generated than needed; and rapid-response gas generators until all the other pieces are slotted into place.

How much is needed

And of course, electricity production is only a fraction of our energy use. We also use energy for transport, agriculture, industry and heating our buildings, and to produce exports.

How do we total up what we will need in the way of electricity to replace fossil fuels across all these sectors? Unfortunately, comparison of different energy sources is not straightforward. Electricity from a solar panel is ready to be used. However, the chemical energy in coal, oil or natural gas has to be converted into a useful form, such as steam or electricity. Much of the energy in these fossil fuels is lost in the conversion to useful energy.

Figure 6: Australia's energy consumption by source

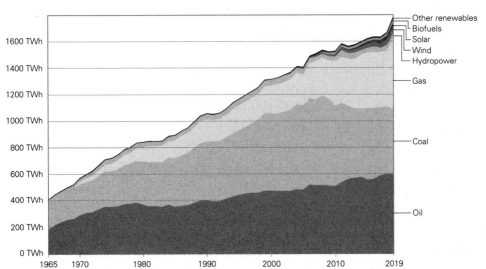

Source: *Our World in Data*, based on *BP Statistical Review of World Energy*.
Notes: The data in this figure have been adjusted by the substitution method to account for the energy lost when fossil fuels are converted into usable energy. 'Other renewables' includes geothermal, biomass and waste energy.

The way to compare energy consumption between fuel types is the "substitution method." This takes into account the relative efficiency of conversion. For example, if a particular coal-fired electricity generator manages to convert one-third of the chemical energy in the coal into electricity while losing the other two-thirds as waste heat, in the substitution method we consider only the one-third that becomes electricity to be useful energy. That is, the method scales all the data about energy consumption so that we compare the output of solar, wind and hydroelectric generators to the useful energy output from fossil fuels. The substitution method is only an approximation for the very many and complex ways that fossil fuels are currently used for useful energy, but it is helpful for arriving at a ballpark estimate of our future electricity needs.

Using the substitution method, solar and wind production in Australia in 2019 contributed 2.5 per cent and 2.7 per cent, respectively, for a total of 5.2 per cent of our entire energy needs.

Now it is time to look at the big picture. If we imagine that our total domestic energy needs were overnight shifted to electricity, and that by the substitution method solar and wind already contribute 5.2 per cent of Australia's total energy, we would need to increase solar and wind production in Australia by a factor of nearly twenty for our domestic energy needs to be met by clean electricity.

We have already seen that an approximate sevenfold increase in solar and wind electrical energy would achieve 100 per cent renewables for our existing electricity requirements. Thus, a further factor of nearly three would achieve the all-up multiplier of twenty to meet our total domestic energy needs. That is, we would need to generate electricity in future at about 300 per cent the level we generate electricity from all sources today to achieve an "all-electric Australia." This factor of 300 per cent is an approximation, but gives us a feel for the magnitude of the task.

In 2019, our cumulative installed solar and wind capacity was 23.2 gigawatts. So twenty times more than that, on the existing ratio of solar to wind, would be approximately 460 gigawatts. If that turns out to be the needed level, and if the solar and wind generators have a 25-year life, there will be continuous replacement of about 18 gigawatts annually. This is only three times the current rate of installation and quite reasonable, given that it would be servicing our total energy needs, not just the electricity sector.

THE STORAGE CONUNDRUM

We've all heard the concern, expressed again and again: "How will a future renewable-energy electricity system cope when the sun isn't shining and the wind isn't blowing?" The answer is almost biblical: store the electrical energy when it is abundant, for use when there is famine. The technical term for supplying the shortfall is "firming." The need for firming arises on a daily basis, and to overcome infrequent but potentially lengthy weather-related drops in electrical output.

Battery storage

Everybody is talking about batteries. And rightly so, because like solar and wind electricity, battery prices are dropping, their availability is soaring, and their reliability and performance keep on improving. The type of battery technology that is on the tip of those wagging tongues is the lithium ion rechargeable battery.

There are many different types of rechargeable battery. The workhorse for more than 150 years has been the lead acid battery, still in use today, most commonly in vehicles for the starter motor and accessories. Another classic, introduced for consumer devices such as remote-control cars and early mobile phones, is the nickel cadmium battery, but it is rarely used today because cadmium is toxic and the batteries suffer from a memory effect that means that if they are not fully depleted before being recharged, their capacity diminishes. Their replacement in many electronic devices today is the nickel metal hydride battery. This battery is more environmentally friendly and suffers less from the memory effect than the nickel cadmium battery it replaces.

But starting in the early 1990s, we entered the age of lithium ion rechargeable batteries. At first, they were used for portable consumer electronic devices, such as toys, phones, model aeroplanes and laptop computers. They store more energy per kilogram than other battery types, store more energy per litre, are less susceptible to the memory effect and can discharge their stored energy very quickly. Eventually, they made their way into the ultimate portable consumer product: the electric car. When Tesla co-founder Elon Musk oversaw the production of the first Tesla Roadster in 2008, he redefined the concept of an electric car. Previously, electric cars used lead acid batteries, with the result that the cars were heavy and short-range. In contrast, the Roadster used lithium ion batteries to give it more than 300 kilometres range and a dramatic acceleration from zero to 100 kilometres per hour in less than four seconds. Now, we are seeing an explosion of available electric car models, ranging from urban runabouts to powerful SUVs. All of them use lithium ion batteries.

The wide adoption of lithium ion batteries in electronic devices and electric vehicles, where their light weight and small volume are critically important, has resulted in ever-increasing numbers being manufactured at ever-diminishing prices. The rate that prices have fallen is stunning. In 2010, the average price of a battery pack for automotive use was US$1183 per kilowatt-hour. By 2019 that had fallen to US$156, and Japan has set a target for the price to fall to US$97 or less by 2030. Battery systems for grid-scale applications are more expensive but following a similar steep decline.

Light weight and small volume might not be important properties of batteries for storing electricity in the electricity grid, but price and performance are. In 2012, the first grid-scale lithium ion battery was commissioned in California. It was a 5-megawatt, 1.25-megawatt-hour battery that could run for just fifteen minutes at full power. Fast-forward to 2017: after the statewide blackout the year before, the South Australian government contracted with the Tesla corporation to build the world's biggest battery, a 100-megawatt, 129-megawatt-hour battery that could run for an hour and a quarter at full power. Since then, it is lithium ion batteries everywhere, in Australia and internationally.

What makes lithium special? For a start, it is the lightest of all metals, sitting immediately after hydrogen and helium in the periodic table. Further, of the metals commonly used for batteries, lithium has the highest electrode potential – the voltage difference between the negative and the positive terminal. As a result of being light and having a high electrode potential, batteries using lithium have the highest energy storage per kilogram. And lithium is environmentally harmless and not toxic to humans. On that last point, it is worth noting that lithium carbonate salt has been routinely used for more than fifty years as a medicine to treat bipolar disorder.

While lithium ion batteries are very good, they are not perfect. One problem is that, like all batteries, they lose peak capacity after a few years of operation. However, their operational life is estimated to be better than ten years in electric cars and is getting better with each refinement to the manufacturing process. Another challenge is that because they store so much energy per unit volume, battery packs must be made with complex protection circuits to limit overheating. Where that has not been the case, fires have resulted. But scientists, engineers and manufacturers are constantly learning, with the result that battery fires are rare. In a 2017 study, the National Highway Traffic Safety Administration in the United States concluded that the risk is probably slightly less than the risk of fire in a petrol or diesel vehicle and the consequences should be less harmful because of the lesser amount of flammable fuel released.

Lithium ion batteries are an economic opportunity for Australia. In 2006, our lithium mining production was less than 5000 tonnes. In 2018, production reached 51,000 tonnes, and although our lithium reserves are only a third that of Chile, Australia was by far the world's largest exporter of lithium.

There are other modern battery chemistries, including batteries that store energy by charge separation in liquids. These include vanadium redox batteries – invented in Australia – and sodium-bromine batteries. While both of these technologies scale well to large size, they have not come down in cost at the same rate as lithium ion batteries and have not captured a significant market share. At the time of writing this essay, lithium ion batteries dominate the world of batteries and there is no indication that they will yield primacy any time soon.

Batteries for grid storage are used in two different ways. The first role is provision of grid-support services. Imagine a system where a large generator fails. As quickly as possible, other generators have to step in to supply the load. But if the other generators are solar, they can't, because their output is determined by the sunshine. However, a battery can nearly instantly increase its output to supply the load, thereby securing the ongoing operation of the electricity system. Till recently, providing system security like in this example has been the main function of large, grid-scale batteries, such as the Tesla battery in South Australia.

The second role is energy storage. Late in 2020, AGL announced that it will build a 250-megawatt, 1000-megawatt-hour battery that can operate for four hours at full power, at Torrens Island in South Australia. The long duration and high capacity of this battery will make it functionally competitive with gas generators to meet electricity demand in peak periods. Also late in 2020, French renewable energy company Neoen, in partnership with Tesla, won a contract from the Victorian government to build Australia's highest-power battery at Geelong, rated at 300 megawatts, 450 megawatt-hours, able to dispatch electricity at full power for 1.5 hours. It is scheduled to be finished by the end of the year. And this is just the beginning.

Here I pause to ask: how often have you seen a headline such as "200-megawatt battery to be installed next year"? What does it mean? Basically, it is meaningless, because it takes two parameters to specify a battery: the power and the stored energy. To specify just the power is like describing a runner as being the fastest, without saying whether she specialises in 100-metre sprints or 42-kilometre marathons.

The proper way to specify a grid-scale battery is in megawatts – the power – and in megawatt-hours – the stored energy. The latter tells you exactly how long the battery can run at full power. Thus, a 5-megawatt, 15-megawatt-hour battery could operate at full power for three hours.

There is nothing wrong with a battery or other storage device having a short duration in some applications. For example, to supply a power boost for a few seconds in a hydrogen-powered electric vehicle, special storage devices called super capacitors can be used. They have high instantaneous power, but they can only supply that power for a few seconds, or a minute at most. To provide system security to the electricity grid, a high-power battery need only have sufficient storage to supply the rated power for a few minutes.

Pumped hydro storage

There is another important form of electricity storage that has been in widespread use for a lot longer than batteries: pumped hydro. The principle is simple. Take two small dams. Use electricity from the grid to pump water from the lower dam to the upper dam. The electrical energy used to pump the water uphill is converted into gravitational potential energy. That provides the energy storage. When the system needs electricity, let the water flow from the upper dam to the lower dam, converting the gravitational potential energy back into electrical energy.

This works for two reasons, one steeped in the laws of physics, the other in the laws of markets. The relevant law of physics is the law of the conservation of energy, which states that energy can neither be created nor destroyed, but can be converted from one form of energy to another. In pumped hydro, electrical energy is converted to gravitational potential energy and back again. Similarly, in an electric car, the electrochemical energy in the battery is converted into electrical energy that is used to drive the motor and impart kinetic energy to the car. When it is time to slow down, the regenerative braking system converts the kinetic energy back into electrical energy that is used to top up the electrochemical energy in the battery.

It sounds ideal, and it is nearly so. The nuisance is that every time there is a conversion from one form of energy to another, some of the energy turns into forms that are not convenient to reuse, such as heat energy, light energy or sound energy. In pumped hydro storage, the main losses are as heat. The round-trip efficiency, describing what fraction of the initial electrical energy can be recovered after pumping the water uphill and allowing it to power a generator on the way down, is between 70 per cent and 80 per cent. The round-trip efficiency of grid-scale lithium ion batteries is between 85 per cent and 95 per cent (including the losses in the electronics used to convert the alternating current from the grid into the direct current required to charge the battery, and the electronics used in reverse when discharging).

The relevant law of markets is the law of arbitrage. It is not as formal as a law of physics, but is important nevertheless. Simply put, the law of arbitrage is buy low, sell high. For example, if there is more electricity being generated in the middle of the day than is needed by consumers, the operator of a grid battery or pumped hydro facility will be able to purchase electricity at a low price. Then, in the evening, after the sun goes down and the demand is strong, the storage operator will be able to sell at a high price.

By having sufficient storage, supply will be guaranteed, even though the generation sources are variable solar and wind. Further, price extremes will be flattened. The challenge is to have enough storage in the system to ensure reliability, but not so much that the difference between the buying and selling prices shrinks to the point that the storage facilities become uneconomic to operate. The risk is that when selling into the market, the storage system operator has to cover the cost of purchasing the electricity that was stored, the round-trip efficiency losses, repairs, maintenance and capital expenses. If there is too much storage in the system, competition might drive the selling price down to an unsustainable level. It may be that the design of the National Electricity Market will have to evolve to treat electricity delivered from storage differently to electricity delivered from generation.

Globally, pumped hydro storage of 9 million megawatt-hours accounts for 94 per cent of grid storage. The remainder is mostly batteries, and some thermal storage for concentrated solar power.

In Australia, there are three pumped hydro installations: Talbingo in the Snowy Mountains, Shoalhaven in New South Wales, and Wivenhoe near

Brisbane, all built more than thirty-five years ago. Between them, they total 1340 megawatts and 35,000 megawatt-hours of storage, which on average can provide twenty-six hours of full power. The new Snowy 2.0 pumped hydro facility is underway. It is huge, with 2000 megawatts capacity and 350,000 megawatt-hours of storage, for just over seven days of generation at full power.

The majority of storage requirements as we move towards a solar and wind electricity–dominated system will be for up to about eight hours. This is sufficient to cover the late-afternoon and early-evening demand in summer when the sun goes down, or on cold winter mornings. The multi-day storage duration of some pumped hydro facilities will be a saviour for consecutive calm days and overcast skies, but for most of the year will not be used.

Studies at the Australian National University in 2017 demonstrated that Australia has 22,000 potential sites for pumped hydro storage, of which we would need only a tiny fraction to support a 100 per cent renewable electricity system. The authors deliberately restricted their research to sites that were not in national parks and did not involve damming a river. Whether or not some of these are built will depend on market economics, hurdles on permission to build transmission lines, and competition from batteries. A particular advantage of batteries is that they don't need transmission lines because they can be built exactly where they will provide the best outcome, which could sometimes be co-location at a wind farm or solar farm, or sometimes near the load, such as in the basement of a city skyscraper.

Hydrogen storage

It is technically straightforward to use renewable electricity to produce hydrogen and then use the hydrogen at a later time to produce electricity. However, the round-trip efficiency is low: approximately 35 per cent. As a result, hydrogen storage will not be financially competitive with pumped hydro and batteries unless the hydrogen is produced from essentially free electricity from rooftop or other onsite solar panels, or it provides a unique benefit such as ultra-long duration of storage – what is commonly called "seasonal" storage. For example, we might store excess solar electricity in summer for use in winter.

The economics will be most favourable for storage longer than twelve hours and on a very large scale. One way to achieve very low cost per megawatt-hour is to store the hydrogen in giant underground salt caverns or other natural repositories, rather than in tanks. There are half a dozen hydrogen storage caverns already in operation in Texas and the north of England. They are huge. The Advanced Clean Energy Storage project near the city of Delta in Utah is constructing a series of caverns for hydrogen storage by dissolving natural cylindrical salt formations. A typical cavern located more than a kilometre below the surface is 70 metres in diameter and 400 metres tall, sufficient to store pressurised hydrogen holding 150,000 megawatt-hours of energy. Mitsubishi Heavy Industries, one of the partners in this project, estimates that 40,000 shipping containers of lithium ion batteries would be required to store the same amount of energy.

Natural gas

There is another way to support the introduction of large amounts of solar and wind, and that is to use rapid-start natural gas generation. This is a highly flexible, large-scale, on-demand technology to firm solar and wind, which is here and now and meets all the requirements. With natural gas and pumped hydro today, batteries at small scale today but increasingly available, and in the long term some hydrogen storage, we will be able to introduce large amounts of solar and wind stably and manage the daily shortfalls, as well as the rare, prolonged shortfalls.

There is much debate about the use of natural gas as we make the transition to a zero-emissions electricity system. To some extent, some of the discussion is at crosspurposes, because the word "transition" is ambiguous. I now prefer to be specific and talk about natural gas either in a "replacement" or a "firming" role. My comments on the topic have been about the latter – firming – but presumably have been interpreted by some as about the former – replacement.

Replacement is where high-emissions coal-fired electricity generation is shut down and instead provided by lower-emissions natural gas. This approach has been used in some countries and states to enable them to shut down their coal-fired generators. For example, natural gas has replaced a substantial fraction of coal generation in the United States, because it is cheaper and more flexible. This has played a part in the United States reducing its emissions from the electricity sector by 28 per cent between 2005 and 2018.

In Britain, in a major success story, coal-fired electricity production fell from a 67 per cent share in 1990 to just 2 per cent by the end of 2019. At the same time, electricity produced from natural gas increased from virtually zero to nearly 41 per cent, to replace much of the production previously supplied by coal generators.

In South Australia, the last coal-fired generator closed in May 2016. In the two years that followed, to replace that final coal-fired electricity generator, natural gas-fired electricity jumped from 37 per cent to 52 per cent of the annual electricity output. This share is falling, as ever more solar and wind and batteries enter the system, and in the year to June 2020, electricity from natural gas was 43 per cent of the generation in South Australia.

In each of these cases, natural gas was used to replace coal-fired electricity. However, time and technology have moved on. We now have the realistic prospect of replacing coal with the combination of solar, wind and batteries. It can't be done immediately because of the cost and availability of batteries. But if we are prepared to continue to use natural gas for firming, we can be confident of using solar and wind to replace coal generators when they close. With time, less natural gas will be needed for firming and it will eventually be replaced by ever larger, more cost-effective batteries, pumped hydro and, in some cases, stored hydrogen.

In the large east-coast states of Australia, the situation is different from in Britain and South Australia. Take New South Wales as an example. In the year to June 2019, coal-fired electricity was 79 per cent of the annual output and natural gas-fired electricity just 2 per cent. The NSW government has legislated a major shift to solar and wind, signalling it will ultimately exit coal power by shifting the generation mix directly to renewables without using natural gas as a replacement. To achieve this, as well as supporting the commissioning of 12 gigawatts of new solar and wind capacity by 2030, the government will support firming by natural gas and battery storage.

This approach is the quickest way to achieve near-zero emissions. I say "near-zero" because if the annual electricity output was mostly from solar and wind and some hydroelectricity, with gas electricity generation alongside batteries and pumped hydro for firming, the emissions from the gas generators for the small number of hours they would operate, averaged over the course of the year, would be negligible. It is not clear at this time whether existing gas generators will be sufficient to provide firming services.

Market forces will ensure that the use of natural gas is minimised. Put simply, because of the cost of natural gas as a fuel, gas always yields to wind and solar when they are available.

Ultimately, use of natural gas as one of the firming technologies will be replaced by yet more batteries and pumped hydro, or by converting the remaining gas generators to run on hydrogen. The majority of existing natural gas turbines can be modified to run on a hydrogen blend of up to 50 per cent, or in some cases up to 80 per cent.

With new gas generators, should they be installed, they can be designed upfront to be hydrogen-ready. The first example of a hydrogen-ready installation is in Hannibal, Ohio, where a 485-megawatt gas generator is being built to run initially on natural gas blended with 15 per cent hydrogen when it is commissioned at the end of 2021, with the ability to burn 100 per cent clean hydrogen by the end of the decade. The early operations will use industrial by-product hydrogen, but the intention is to use clean hydrogen produced by electrolysis from renewable electricity. Nearby underground salt caverns will be used for large-scale storage of the clean hydrogen.

The near-term and medium-term issue is whether we should allow the pursuit of perfection to get in the way of the very good. Gas generators are able to provide firming services to solar and wind electricity that enable solar and wind to be scaled up very rapidly without risking reliability of supply. That is, we can achieve the very good quickly by using gas in the mix, then approach perfection – zero emissions – as the technology matures.

There is a myth about gas that I should address. This is that if you take into account the upstream fugitive emissions associated with natural gas production, the emissions from a gas-fired generator are worse than from a coal-fired generator. This assertion relies on an unequal comparison. To be a fair comparison, it should take into account the upstream fugitive emissions associated with coal production. For coal, there are upstream methane emissions in mining and crushing. For natural gas, there are upstream methane emissions from the wellhead, handling equipment and pipelines.

A comprehensive analysis titled *Scientific Inquiry into Hydraulic Fracturing*, commissioned by the Northern Territory government, compares coal generators to open-cycle gas turbines that provide rapid-start generation for firming, and shows that gas-fired electricity has 31 per cent lower total emissions, including upstream emissions. The advantage increases to 57 per cent for combined-cycle gas turbines that are used for continuous generation for steady electricity demand. That is, even including upstream emissions, gas-fired electricity is in all cases lower in emissions than coal-fired electricity.

In September 2020, I received a letter from twenty-five scientists, taking issue with my expectation that natural gas will be a part of Australia's energy mix for many years to come. The scientists want to phase out gas as quickly as possible and insist there is no place for expanded gas infrastructure in Australia, given the significant contribution of gas to carbon dioxide emissions. Where we differ is not the science; where we differ is in what we regard as a realistic way forward. My contention is that the use of gas for firming will allow more solar and wind generation into the electricity grid sooner than otherwise. Gas can ease the way through to the closure of coal-fired power stations. Batteries and pumped hydro will also solve the firming problem, and will be the long-term answer, but natural gas will get us close, more quickly, in the interim. Natural gas can be phased out once hydrogen has been scaled up and commercialised across the spectrum of our energy needs.

One of the authors of the letter said that I was addressing engineering problems, rather than the need to meet the looming Paris temperature limits. It is true: my approach is that of an engineer. My goal is for us to achieve a low-emissions economy as fast as is practicable. And intrinsic to engineering is the realisation that pursuit of perfection does not deliver a finished product. Engineering is the art of optimisation. Design a perfect bridge and it will be too expensive to be built. Compromise the design of a bridge and it will collapse. The job of an engineer is to optimise the design of the bridge. So, too, in everything.

Richard Bolt, a former top public servant who has played a lead role in energy market reform, shares my view that gas has a role. In September, he wrote that using natural gas as a backup would help Australia meet its emissions targets: "It will accelerate emission reductions, because an increasingly renewable and reliable power supply will allow coal generators to be closed early and safely. Natural gas use is modest when used for back-up power, so will produce low emissions while bringing forward much larger emission cuts from the coal closures." Further, natural gas can eventually be replaced in peaking generators with clean hydrogen.

HYDROGEN – THE HERO OF OUR STORY?

To this point, the discussion has focused on eliminating the emissions from Australia's electricity supply, which currently make up 34 per cent of the country's emissions. We have seen that we can clean up the electricity supply. I take a detour now to introduce hydrogen, a near-miraculous fuel that could play a major part in eliminating many of the remaining sources of emissions.

There are several reasons why hydrogen should be part of our future zero-emissions energy mix. The first is that hydrogen can be used as an energy carrier in those instances where electrons are not the best way to supply energy, such as for interstate trucking, or exporting renewable energy from Australia to countries as far away as Japan or further. Another is for seasonal storage, as described above. Another is for industrial applications, such as the production of zero-emissions fertilisers and zero-emissions steel. Finally, there is the subtler benefit of resilience through diversity. Today, if the electricity system goes down we can still use natural gas for heating and cooking. Stored hydrogen can provide that surety.

But what is hydrogen? It would be easy to answer that it is a gas that burns, like methane or propane or acetylene. But it is much more special than that. Hydrogen is the first element in the periodic table. It consists of one proton and one electron. Its atomic weight is 1. There is no simpler element. Pure hydrogen exists as a molecule, in which two hydrogen atoms are bound to each other, chemically represented as H_2. At normal temperatures and pressures, yes, it is a gas. It is colourless, odourless, tasteless and non-toxic.

And it burns. Like all fuels, such as wood, petrol, natural gas and alcohol, hydrogen burns by combining with oxygen. What makes it stunningly attractive as we seek to decarbonise the global economy is that when it burns, the end product is water vapour, represented as H_2O. As far as carbon dioxide emissions are concerned, hydrogen is the most attractive fuel of all. Nothing else can compete.

Hydrogen was the first element to form after the big bang at the start of our universe, 13.7 billion years ago. All the other elements formed from hydrogen by fusion and fission events in stars. Even now, after all those billions of years, hydrogen still represents 94 per cent of all the atoms in the universe. Closer to home, hydrogen is the tenth-most abundant element in the Earth's crust.

The difficulty is that hydrogen is not freely available on Earth as it is in stars, and it does not take a genius to realise that the cost of transporting hydrogen from a star, such as our sun, to Earth is, well, astronomical. If hydrogen were as readily available as conventional natural gas, we would have been using it since the start of the industrial revolution. On Earth, there is a tiny amount in our atmosphere, fewer than one hydrogen molecule per million other molecules, too diffuse to be useful. The bulk of our earthly hydrogen is bound to other elements, in hydrocarbons, acids and hydroxides, with the most common place to find hydrogen being in water.

Since we can't drill a hole in the ground to find hydrogen, we have to produce it by a manufacturing process. The simplest and most attractive way to make hydrogen is to use electricity to split water into its constituent components, as in the experiment I hope you did at school. Stick two electrodes into a beaker of water with a touch of added salt. Connect them to a battery. Bubbles start to flow: a pure stream of hydrogen at one electrode and a stream of oxygen at the other. This process is called electrolysis. It is absolutely free of carbon dioxide emissions if the electricity is solar, wind or hydro. This can be done at industrial scale to produce massive quantities of hydrogen. The oxygen is released into the atmosphere. There are some instances where the oxygen can be used for an industrial purpose, such as to improve the efficiency of wastewater purification, but commercial uses of the oxygen are a bonus, not a fundamental.

Hydrogen can also be made from fossil fuels: most commonly from natural gas, but also from coal or oil. However, when hydrogen is made from a fossil fuel, there is a problem: the carbon dioxide by-product. Traditionally, that carbon dioxide has been released to the atmosphere.

Hydrogen produced this way has been used for more than 100 years in industrial processes. Today, hydrogen is used in the tens of millions of tonnes, mostly for refining crude oil into diesel and petrol, but also for making ammonia for fertiliser, and other more minor uses. To meet the global decarbonisation agenda, all existing industrial uses of hydrogen will have to be converted to clean hydrogen, which will either be produced by electrolysis using renewable electricity, or by adding carbon capture and storage to the conventional fossil-fuel processes.

Until recently, pure hydrogen has had no serious role as a fuel, but the idea of hydrogen as a fuel is not new. Indeed, it has a long history. In 1820, the Reverend W. Cecil at Cambridge University was the first to describe an engine that could be powered by burning a mixture of hydrogen gas and air. And in 1842, Welshman William Robert Grove developed the first fuel cell, to produce electricity by combining hydrogen and oxygen. But the most visionary articulation of how hydrogen could be used as a fuel was delivered by Cyrus Harding, the engineer-hero of the 1874 novel *The Mysterious Island*, by French science-fiction writer Jules Verne. In one scene, Mr Harding waxes lyrical to his marooned companions:

> "Yes, but water decomposed into its primitive elements," replied Cyrus Harding, "and decomposed doubtless, by electricity, which will then have become a powerful and manageable force, for all great discoveries, by some inexplicable laws, appear to agree and become complete at the same time. Yes, my friends, I believe that water will one day be employed as fuel, that hydrogen and oxygen which constitute it, used singly or together, will furnish an inexhaustible source of heat and light, of an intensity of which coal is not capable. Someday the coal-rooms of steamers and the tenders of locomotives will, instead of coal, be stored with these two condensed gases, which will burn in the furnaces with enormous calorific power. There is, therefore, nothing to fear. As long as the earth is inhabited it will supply the wants of its inhabitants, and there will

be no want of either light or heat as long as the productions of the vegetable, mineral or animal kingdoms do not fail us. I believe, then, that when the deposits of coal are exhausted we shall heat and warm ourselves with water. Water will be the coal of the future."

What foresight! Hats off to Jules Verne.

Back in the real world, in 1923, British biologist J.B.S. Haldane outlined his vision for a renewable-energy economy powered by "rows of metallic windmills" producing electricity for "electrolytic decomposition of water into oxygen and hydrogen" that would be stored, then recombined, in "oxidation cells" to produce electricity when needed. More foresight!

In the 1940s, wartime interruptions to the oil supply prompted the Queensland government to authorise the construction of a hydrogen plant designed by Australian engineer John Stephens Just, to use off-peak electricity to supply hydrogen for trucks. The war ended, the petrol price fell and the plan became as invisible as the gas itself.

In the 1970s, hydrogen as a fuel surfaced again in response to the oil shock. The term "hydrogen economy" was coined by US chemistry professor John Bockris, in a speech in 1970 and in an article in the journal *Science* in 1972, while he was working at Flinders University in South Australia. Intriguingly, in his *Science* article, Bockris's vision was for floating nuclear generators producing the electricity needed to split water to produce hydrogen.

In the 2000s, hydrogen got a flutter in response to improvements in technology. But consistently, it failed to catch on as fuel. There were many reasons, but high cost was the overwhelming one. Hydrogen was only used as a fuel in special circumstances, where high energy density gave it a special advantage and cost was no object. Perhaps the most prominent use of hydrogen was as the fuel burnt by the main engines in the Space Shuttle, the workhorse US spaceship that for two decades lifted astronauts into space. A much less known use was hydrogen converted into ammonia used as the fuel in the X-15 rocket-powered aeroplane. In 1967, with pilot William Knight at the controls, the X-15 set the world speed record of

7274 kilometres per hour for a human-crewed aeroplane. That record, achieved fifty-four years ago, remains unbroken.

But today, everybody is talking about hydrogen. Why now? First and foremost, because of the global determination to eliminate greenhouse gas emissions. Second, the price to produce clean hydrogen from plentiful solar and wind electricity has plummeted since the turn of the century. There is no other word to describe it. As a result, the price of renewable hydrogen is within a factor of three or four of where it needs to be to compete with fossil fuels, and prospects are good that it will continue to fall rapidly. Third, there has been a steady improvement in the technologies for hydrogen use. For example, the price of fuel cells to convert hydrogen into electricity has come down substantially since the early 2000s, and fuel cells are now smaller, lighter and more robust than they were twenty years ago. Fourth, energy needs to be shipped long distances from countries where it is plentiful to countries where the demand is high. If that energy is to be clean energy, hydrogen and its derivatives, such as ammonia, will be used as the carrier.

It took me a long time to understand the breadth of roles of hydrogen in our future economy. When I worked as the chief technology officer of Better Place Australia, in 2010 and 2011, I was deeply cynical about the prospects of hydrogen as a fuel because it does not have as good round-trip efficiency as battery storage. I looked at hydrogen myopically, for cars and nothing else. Then, during my review of the National Electricity Market, all sorts of industry players and research academics asked me, "What are you going to do for hydrogen, Alan?" My initial answer was that I had no plans whatsoever.

My vision improved a few months later, when, as a member of the Climate Change Authority, I heard a presentation by Ben Wilson, the chair of the gas committee at Energy Networks Australia, in which he described the industry's goal to switch to hydrogen and biogas by 2050. I hadn't previously given thought to how extensively the natural gas industry could be transformed. I went from sceptic to wide-eyed convert. I was inspired to write a column for *Cosmos* magazine about the potential for hydrogen as the fuel of the future. About then, I met Jeff Connolly and Martin Hablutzel, the CEO and head of strategy respectively at Siemens Australia, and their colleague Dr Michael Weinhold, the chief technology officer of the energy division in Germany. They were already thinking deeply about hydrogen as a fuel and the technologies to produce it. Inspired by discussions with them, I put forward the idea to build a "hydrogen city" as one of the national "moonshot" missions in the Industry Innovation and Science Australia strategy.

Soon after, I convened a meeting of a dozen experts from industry, research and government, to discuss topics ranging from safe use of hydrogen in our homes through to liquefaction for export. We shared our mutual excitement, but I wasn't sure how to proceed. Eventually, in February 2018, I contacted energy minister Josh Frydenberg and offered him a briefing. He, quite reasonably, had no starting interest, but being a curious man and prepared to hear me out after my work chairing the electricity review, he invited me to his office. Intrigued by what he learnt, he asked me to present a briefing document to one of the upcoming meetings of the state, territory and Commonwealth energy ministers.

I tapped into my cohort of experts again, and instead of the five-page formal document the minister was probably expecting, we produced a sixty-page glossy vision statement called *Hydrogen for Australia's Future*. The ministers loved it and asked me to come back to their next meeting with an outline of how we could develop a national hydrogen strategy. The next meeting, chaired by the new Commonwealth energy minister, Angus Taylor, authorised the development of the strategy, and the rest is history.

Some would say that I am now an evangelist, but I would argue that I have an objective, evidence-based view on the prospects for hydrogen to contribute to our low-emissions future. Just as silicon is an element with unique properties that make it dominant as the backbone of the electronics industry, and just as lithium is an element with unique properties that make it supreme as the backbone of the battery industry, so too is hydrogen an element with unique properties that will make it excel as the backbone of the future fuels industry.

The challenge of hydrogen? Producing it. Unlike coal, oil, natural gas, nuclear, water in big dams, wind or solar, which are fuels ready to use, it takes energy to produce hydrogen for use as a fuel. You could think of all the others as primary energy sources, and hydrogen as a secondary energy source, or an energy carrier.

Hydrogen can be produced by electrolysis or from fossil fuels. Given that hydrogen has to be produced, it is not clear to me in what sector of the economy it belongs. Hydrogen is a manufactured product, like a battery. It is an energy fuel, like coal or oil. And it is a resource that can be exported. This versatility is part of its magic. I'll leave it to economists to work out where it conceptually belongs.

Hydrogen from electrolysis

The two ingredients to make hydrogen by electrolysis are electricity and water. To do it at large scale – say, at the scale of our liquefied natural gas industry – takes lots of electricity and a good deal of water. For those of a technical bent, it takes 39.4 kilowatt-hours of electrical energy and 9 litres of water to produce 1 kilogram of hydrogen. When burnt, except in special circumstances, all the water is returned to the atmosphere, but only 33.3 kilowatt hours of energy is available to do useful things, such as power a truck. The 6.1 kilowatt-hours difference is lost as waste heat that cannot be easily recovered.

The numbers involved in building future hydrogen industries are quite stunning. Let's take a moment to think about hydrogen for future export. If we were to export as much hydrogen by energy value as Australia's 79 million tonnes of liquefied natural gas (LNG) exports in the year to June 2020, because of the superior mass energy density of hydrogen we would have to export 33 million tonnes.

On my calculations, the electricity required to produce 33 million tonnes of hydrogen for export, including the electricity for handling and liquefying, would be approximately 2200 terawatt-hours. This is about eight times Australia's total electricity generation in 2019.

To produce that electrical energy from solar, we would need to install nearly 1000 gigawatts of capacity, which is seventy-five times more than Australia's installed solar capacity in 2019. It is more than the installed solar capacity worldwide. The solar fields would cover about 20,000 square kilometres of land. That's about four-fifths of the size of our biggest cattle farm, Anna Creek Station, in South Australia, but only about 0.25 per cent of Australia's landmass.

So, yes, it's a big requirement, but phased in over thirty years, it's quite conceivable. Because of the superior capacity factor of wind, if the electricity came from a mix of wind and solar the installed capacity would be smaller, perhaps 700 gigawatts or thereabouts.

Australia is richly endowed with sun, wind and land – sufficiently so that if the construction costs are low and the land is made available, we can produce all the solar and wind electricity we would need to support a large-scale hydrogen export industry.

But what about water? Australia is a dry continent and water is a precious resource. The amount needed for a large export industry is considerable, but not unusual for other large-scale industries. For example, the National Hydrogen Strategy calculated that for Australia to be a major supplier of a large-scale global hydrogen industry in 2050, the water consumption would be equivalent to one-third of the water now used by the Australian mining industry. This sounds like a manageable amount, but the distribution of the water supplies might not always be convenient. Fortunately, we have access to water supplies that could not otherwise be used for human consumption or in agriculture, such as wastewater, salty artesian water and seawater. It turns out that using modern reverse-osmosis desalination methods, the cost to produce clean water to be used in the electrolysis process would only add a couple of cents to the cost of producing a kilogram of hydrogen.

When hydrogen is made from water electrolysis, the production and use of the hydrogen and the by-product oxygen is a completely closed cycle. For every molecule of oxygen released to the atmosphere, somewhere in the world a molecule of oxygen will be combined with two molecules of hydrogen to produce water again. The only losers are the photons in the sunlight that hit the solar panel, but at least they will not perish in vain hitting the ground.

A significant technical challenge in the use of hydrogen, however, is efficiency, both in production and use. Not all of the electrical energy used to split water into oxygen and hydrogen is converted into the chemical energy of the hydrogen. Similarly, when hydrogen is burnt or directly converted back into electricity, energy is lost in the process. It has been estimated that in 2050 more than US$1 trillion worth of hydrogen might be consumed. If, in the coming decades, the overall electrolysis production and distribution efficiency can be improved by 10 per cent, that would correspond to a global savings of US$100 billion. That's a challenge that an army of scientists and engineers are already gladly addressing, and they will continue to work on incremental improvements for decades to come.

The operation of most electrolysis units can be ramped up and down very quickly, in seconds for some designs and minutes for others. Since the hydrogen they produce is being compressed to send down pipelines or to store in tanks, the production is quite decoupled from the use, and there is no harm done by curtailing production from time to time.

Because of this, producing hydrogen through electrolysis can help the National Electricity Market in two ways. First, when hydrogen production is supplied by electricity from the grid the electrolysis units can be ramped up and down to match variable production from solar and wind. Industrial-scale hydrogen producers will be able to buy solar and wind electricity for very low prices by agreeing to curtail their use whenever supply is tight. Second, imagine a large remote hydrogen production facility a long way from one of our major electricity grids. Let's suppose that it is a facility with a mix of solar and wind. If the developer were encouraged to build a long-distance transmission line to carry a small fraction of the facility's peak generation back to the national grid, it would likely have enough output even on low output days to supply the grid with electricity. This would substantially reduce the need for battery storage on the grid. The operator of the hydrogen production facility would be able to charge a higher price for electricity sold to grid customers than the internal price charged for hydrogen production, so this would be a win-win arrangement.

Hydrogen from fossil fuels

The other way to make hydrogen is from fossil fuels. That is the way that hydrogen is mostly made today for existing industrial processes. Although hydrogen itself produces no emissions when burnt, if it is made from natural gas or coal and the carbon dioxide by-product is not captured and permanently stored with carbon capture and storage, then the emissions completely negate any benefit. Thus, there is a clear requirement that in future, when hydrogen is made from fossil fuels, the carbon dioxide must be captured and permanently stored.

The main criticism directed at producing hydrogen from fossil fuels is that it will proceed without carbon capture and storage. Wrong. There are two reasons why this will not be the case. First, there will be no buyers. No country or company is going to import or use hydrogen that is more expensive than the fossil fuels it is replacing unless it meets the environmental objective to be clean hydrogen. The Japanese consortium operating in Victoria is confident it can implement highly effective CCS. If it can, it will have a market for its hydrogen. If it cannot, there will be no market and it will not proceed.

Second, the world will adopt a certification scheme. This will reliably monitor the production process and issue certificates for every kilogram of hydrogen to track how much carbon dioxide was released during production. If the emissions exceed a threshold acceptable to the importing country, that hydrogen will be rejected. Australia is currently engaged with other countries to develop an internationally agreed certification scheme. Ideally, the certification scheme will be based on numbers, not colours. The existing colour code that refers to brown, blue, green and other colours of hydrogen is emotive rather than focused on the only thing that counts: atmospheric emissions of carbon dioxide.

When hydrogen is made from natural gas, about a third of the original energy in the natural gas is lost in the production process. But that is a small price to pay for eliminating the carbon dioxide emissions that would occur if the natural gas were to be directly burnt in millions of homes and factories.

Fuel diversity

An advantage of producing hydrogen from fossil fuels with carbon capture and permanent storage is that it adds diversity to our future energy supply. It avoids placing all our eggs in one basket. If the current use of fossil fuels is replaced solely by new solar and wind electricity, we will have replaced an array of seven large-scale primary energy sources (coal, oil, natural gas, hydroelectricity, nuclear, solar and wind) with just two. True, we will never run out of sunshine and wind. However, the lack of diversity is an in-principle concern, and there might be rare weather conditions that reduce solar and wind production across large geographical regions for days at a time.

Another reason we should stay open-minded about producing hydrogen with CCS – if it is proven commercially viable – is to reduce the quantity of solar and wind generation ultimately required to provide for all our energy needs. Producing renewable hydrogen is inherently inefficient, so if all our clean hydrogen comes from solar and wind electricity, we will need to build a lot more solar and wind farms than otherwise, using large quantities of land, copper, concrete, steel and critical minerals.

The commercial challenge for hydrogen – building demand

To become a large-scale fuel contributing to our low-emissions future, clean hydrogen has to match the price, or nearly so, of the incumbent fossil fuels.

The global Hydrogen Council, established by leading energy, transport and industry companies, commissioned a study from McKinsey & Company, published in January 2020, that projected the price of producing hydrogen from renewable electricity could fall 60 per cent by 2030 – from

US$6 to US$2.60 per kilogram. At this price, hydrogen would be competitive with conventional fossil fuels for long-distance trucks and trains, and with renewable electricity for high-temperature industrial heating.

If the engineering challenge for hydrogen is to produce it cost-effectively, the commercial challenge is to build demand. Today, there is an imbalance of supply and demand. Australian developers and investors are poised to build gigantic hydrogen production facilities and can do so in just a few years from financial commitment to first production. For example, the Asian Renewable Energy Hub is a 26-gigawatt wind and solar generation facility in Western Australia, which will produce up to 3 gigawatts for use as electricity for mining companies in the Pilbara region and the balance for large-scale production of clean hydrogen and ammonia for export.

However, building demand is complicated. Take trucks, for example. It takes a few years to design a new truck, another few years to test prototypes with customers, and more time still to construct a new production line. Even then, customers will only buy the new trucks at the replacement rate of their existing fleet. It will literally take a decade or two to build substantial demand for hydrogen for road transport. A small number of passenger ferries are being built in Europe, and in our own backyard, in Queensland. But these take many years from concept to launch, and then significant time to enter the fleet in large numbers. So while their adoption is likely, it will take time.

Some uses, though, will be quicker. Blending 10 per cent hydrogen into the gas distribution network could be done relatively quickly. It is not that hard to do, because in Australia the gas distribution pipes in our major cities are already made from polyethylene, which happens to be hydrogen-compatible. Blending hydrogen at this level would not require any changes to consumer appliances, and could be done at very little cost to the consumer. The industry would gain enormous experience, and costs would decline because of the production scale.

Similarly, if industries such as oil refining and ammonia production that already use hydrogen produced from fossil fuels without CCS were required to use clean hydrogen, that would build demand very quickly.

The question I am most often asked about hydrogen in the economy of the future is: how quickly will it develop? My answer is: be ambitious, be patient. Ambitious, so that we capture the potential. Patient, because transforming global energy systems takes time. It took approximately thirty years from 1989, when the first drop of liquefied natural gas shipped from Australian shores, to the point of our vying with Qatar to be the world's biggest exporter. And the planning started ten years earlier, in 1979. In the chairman's note at the front of the National Hydrogen Strategy, I wrote: "Around the planet the pace of research, demonstrations, product development and pilot projects is accelerating, seemingly by the day. For the anxious, progress is too slow, but look back a few decades from now and history will record the hydrogen industry as an overnight success."

State and territory governments around the country have introduced funded hydrogen action plans, teams have been established to ensure their effective rollout, and more than $500 million has been committed to the hydrogen industry by the Commonwealth government in the past few years.

Individual companies are stepping up too, as rousingly outlined by Andrew Forrest, chairman of Fortescue Metals Group, in his Boyer Lecture for the ABC in January. Fortescue is thinking big: hundreds of gigawatts of renewable electricity to produce hydrogen, commencement of a pilot plant this year to make zero-emissions steel, and planning to convert their trucks and trains and ships to run on clean hydrogen or its ammonia derivative.

The National Hydrogen Strategy identified clear measures of success by 2030, such as: an exemplary safety record; Australia being a top three supplier to Asia; economic benefits for Australians; and an international certificate of origin scheme in place to prove the provenance and production quality of each kilogram of hydrogen produced.

It is worth a few words here on how the National Hydrogen Strategy was developed. Most reviews or reports consult widely, then reviewers hunker down and write a report to present to government. The government responds to the recommendations, choosing which ones to adopt and fund. In contrast, instead of being a report to government, on the suggestion of senior public servants, the National Hydrogen Strategy was developed as a creature of government – all governments, not just the Commonwealth. I chaired the steering committee and the stakeholders advisory group. We consulted with ministers and departmental staff in all jurisdictions all the way through. It was a complex logistical undertaking, but the benefit was that the final report was already substantially agreed to by the state, territory and Commonwealth governments before the meeting that adopted it. There were no recommendations. Instead, there were fifty-seven agreed actions. Every one of the agreed actions was adopted, including an implementation team to ensure their delivery. It was an unusual approach, but not unique. What may have been unique is that this was the only time anybody I asked could remember that the state, territory and Commonwealth governments adopted a strategy to build an industry that did not already exist.

SHIPPING SUNSHINE

Australia is a huge exporter of energy, primarily in the form of coal and natural gas. But if worldwide demand for these vanishes, what are our future energy export prospects? Potentially huge. There is no reason why Australia should not be one of the most successful exporters of renewable energy in the world. There are three ways we can export vast amounts of renewable energy to replace these fossil-fuel exports.

First, directly as electricity, via undersea cables to Singapore and Indonesia and other proximal countries in Southeast Asia. Australian company Sun Cable has proposed a 3-gigawatt undersea cable to Singapore and eventually Indonesia, with exports commencing in 2027. The project has been granted major project status by the Australian government. There is a single-point-of-failure risk with undersea cables, but this is manageable, given the careful technology planning and the long trading history between Australia and Singapore.

The second way we can export renewable energy is by shipping hydrogen and its derivatives, such as ammonia. I call this "shipping sunshine." When hydrogen is produced from solar electricity and sent abroad, it is obviously shipping sunshine, but what if the hydrogen is made from wind or hydroelectricity? Well, wind is driven by variations of air pressure, which are caused by differential heating of large areas of land and sea by sunshine. And sunshine striking water warms it up, causing evaporation and ultimately rain and hydroelectricity.

In a country such as Australia, other than for backup, using hydrogen to generate electricity makes no sense because we have plenty of electricity in the first place. But in Japan, where 94 per cent of energy needs are imported as coal, oil or natural gas, importing clean hydrogen or clean ammonia to generate electricity is eminently sensible. And increasingly so. Two years ago, Japan planned to import 300,000 tonnes of hydrogen by 2030 – roughly enough to run a 1-gigawatt generator continuously for a year. Just recently, Japan upped its plans to 3 million tonnes of hydrogen by 2030, enough to run ten 1-gigawatt generators, which might be needed in lieu of Japan continuing operation of its reduced nuclear fleet.

The logistics involved in shipping hydrogen are complex, but can be seen as an extension of shipping liquefied natural gas. Natural gas has to be cooled to −161°C before it liquefies. That's extremely cold. Hydrogen has to be cooled to −253°C before it liquefies. That's exceptionally cold! The coldest temperature for any material is −273°C. There is no possibility of cooling any further, because at that temperature the molecules of which the material is composed stop moving – no jiggling; no kinetic energy; no temperature. The Celsius (°C) temperature scale we use day to day is an arbitrary scale in which zero is the freezing point of water. The temperature scale used in physics is one in which zero is the absolute coldest state of matter. It is sometimes called the absolute temperature scale, and more formally the Kelvin temperature scale, named after Lord Kelvin, who in 1848 determined absolute zero (and in 1892 became the first scientist to sit in the House of Lords).

So, hydrogen has to be cooled to 20°C in the absolute temperature scale. That's not easy, but it is routinely done. The amount of electricity required to run the pumps and compressors for cooling is as much as 40 per cent of the amount of energy stored in the hydrogen, but if the compression takes place in Australia, rich in renewable electricity, the cost is not overly high. At the destination, which is the energy-poor importing country, virtually no energy is required for gasifying the liquefied hydrogen. It literally evaporates into the distribution pipes.

In between, there is the need for special ships that can keep the liquefied hydrogen in its ultracool, liquid state, without having to run energy-hungry onboard cooling systems. To meet this requirement, these ships need special insulated tanks. The first such ship, the *Suiso Frontier*, was launched by Kawasaki Heavy Industries in Kobe, Japan, in December 2019. I was there as a guest. It was my first and only attendance at the launch of a big ship. At a ship launch, it is easy to be overwhelmed by the sheer scale of the vessel. In this case, it was also exciting to know that this was the first vessel of its kind ever to be built and launched. But the most overwhelming feeling of all was the realisation that the launch represented the beginning of a new era. I sent myself a postcard with a picture of the *Suiso Frontier* from Kobe to my home address in Melbourne. On it, I wrote: "I have witnessed not just the launch of a ship, but the beginning of a new era, in which humankind can send renewable energy between the continents."

Alternatively, the hydrogen can be exported by combining it with nitrogen from the atmosphere to make ammonia. Ammonia is easy to handle, and ships capable of carrying ammonia already plough the waters on a regular basis. At the destination, the ammonia can either be used as an industrial fuel, or it can be split by catalysts back to hydrogen and nitrogen. Separating the hydrogen from the mixture is not easy, but a breakthrough invention by the CSIRO to use vanadium membranes to filter out the hydrogen has significant global potential.

Another way to export the hydrogen is bound to a metal to form a metal hydride. This has long been investigated but has been hampered by the high temperatures required for charging and discharging. A recent breakthrough at the University of New South Wales has seen the initial commercialisation, by a company named LAVO, of a room-temperature metal hydride storage system.

The third way we can export renewable energy is as embodied energy, in products such as steel, aluminium and fertiliser. Take steel. Renewable electricity can replace metallurgical coal for melting the iron ore. In addition to providing heat, the carbon in coal is used as a chemical reducing agent, to "reduce" the iron oxide to elemental iron. That is, each carbon atom in the coal binds two oxygen atoms in the iron oxide and sacrifices itself to a new life as a carbon dioxide molecule. Some of the carbon remains bound to the iron to make steel, which is actually an alloy of iron and carbon. Alternatively, hydrogen can make the same sacrifice, binding with oxygen to become a water molecule, thereby reducing the iron ore to elemental iron. In this case, further processing in an electric arc furnace is used to produce steel. Thus, if we were to build an export steel industry in Australia, we would upgrade our iron ore into steel consisting of iron from our ore, electrical energy for heating, and hydrogen used as a chemical reducing agent. Another possible pathway to zero-emissions steel is called molten oxide electrolysis. In this case, iron ore is dissolved in a liquid silicon dioxide electrolyte at the very high temperature of about 1600°C. An electric current is passed through the mixture and the iron ore is reduced to liquid iron, to be followed by processing in an electric arc furnace to make steel.

Given that we have all three ingredients for making zero-emissions steel – iron ore, renewable electricity, clean hydrogen – the economic case for adding value to our iron ore rather than shipping it is attractive. In May 2020, Tony Wood and colleagues at the Grattan Institute made the case that "Australia has an historic opportunity to create a multi-billion-dollar, export-focused manufacturing sector based on globally competitive renewable energy."

Aluminium is another potential zero-emissions export. The refining of alumina to zero-emissions aluminium requires a huge amount of solar, wind or hydroelectricity: 15 megawatt-hours per tonne of aluminium produced. Indeed, this is such a large amount of electrical energy that aluminium is often referred to as congealed electricity. If the electricity is generated from solar or wind energy, countries such as Australia, which have both the raw ingredients and the renewable electricity, should have an economic advantage in refining the aluminium onshore. The challenge of shifting to solar or wind to provide the electricity is constancy. Aluminium smelters suffer irreversible damage if the electricity is interrupted for more than a few hours, so the variable supply has to be firmed while keeping the average price low.

Shifting to renewable electricity would eliminate 90 per cent of the emissions from our existing aluminium smelters. The last 10 per cent reduction would come from replacing the carbon electrodes, which are consumed during smelting, with inert electrodes. This is harder than it sounds, but a lot of research and development is underway internationally, and demonstration production using ceramic anodes has been shown through a partnership between Alcoa and Rio Tinto as the producers, and Apple Inc. as the customer. Emissions from producing 20 million tonnes of aluminium in 2019 constituted 4 per cent of Australia's emissions. This is a significant percentage, which is why production of low-emissions aluminium was identified as a priority in the Low Emissions Technology Statement.

For fertiliser, clean hydrogen can be combined with nitrogen from the air to produce clean ammonia, which can then be used to produce the nitrates that are the main chemical feedstock for fertiliser. It's too soon to say, but the market for zero-emissions fertiliser might be very large in future.

All of these are examples of what Ross Garnaut calls Australia's opportunity to become a low-carbon energy superpower.

After electricity, the stationary energy sector is the next biggest source of greenhouse gas emissions in Australia. There are too many contributors to stationary energy to look at them all, so I will focus on the biggest emitters. In 2020, 102 million tonnes of carbon dioxide equivalent came from five major activities: manufacturing, energy, buildings, mining, and agriculture, forestry and fishing.

The **manufacturing** subsector contributes 30 million tonnes of emissions. Nearly 40 per cent of this, 11 million tonnes, comes from alumina production. The aluminium ore in the ground is called bauxite. Australia is the world's largest producer of bauxite, and we export about one-third of our production. The other two-thirds is converted into alumina, of which we export approximately 85 per cent of our production. The remaining 15 per cent is refined into aluminium. The energy used in bauxite production is accounted for in the mining subsector, and the energy used in aluminium smelting is accounted for in the electricity sector. That leaves alumina production to be accounted for in the manufacturing subsector. The stationary energy usage is in process steps with almost biological names: digestion, clarification, precipitation and calcination. Emissions reduction will come from improved efficiency, and eventually fuel switching to renewable electricity for steam production.

After alumina production, the next most emissions-intensive segment in manufacturing is the chemicals industry, with fuel-related emissions sitting at 8 million tonnes. The industry produces industrial gases, fertilisers, paints, plastic and foam products, adhesives, surface cleaners, toiletries, detergents, pesticides and pharmaceuticals. Most of the 9 million tonnes are emitted from burning fossil fuels to create heat used directly and for the production of steam. Significant commitment from the industry will be required to replace fossil-fuel heating with renewable electricity and clean hydrogen.

The **energy** subsector contributes 27 million tonnes of emissions. Approximately 70 per cent of emissions in this subsector are related to liquefied natural gas processing, in particular, power generation for compression, pumping and refrigeration. The solution is to shift to renewable electricity. Woodside has already signalled its intention to make this shift at its Karratha processing plant, using solar electricity and battery firming, with a small amount of gas generation when necessary.

The **building** subsector contributes 19 million tonnes of emissions. This is mostly the use of natural gas in residential and commercial buildings for heating, hot water and cooking. In the coming decade, emissions in this subsector are projected to fall slightly due to energy efficiency measures. In the long term, all of the emissions in this subsector could be eliminated by replacing natural gas with renewable electricity and clean hydrogen.

The **mining** subsector also contributes 19 million tonnes of emissions. Large quantities of diesel fuel are used either directly in, or to generate electricity for, the excavators, crushers, bulldozers, conveyors and facilities. In addition to producing emissions, diesel fuel at remote sites is expensive. For both reasons, Australian mining companies are motivated to use on-site solar with storage for direct use as electricity in so-called "microgrids," and for production of hydrogen for direct use in heavy vehicles and for seasonal storage. However, it is still early days.

The **agriculture, forestry and fishing** subsector contributes 7 million tonnes of emissions. This is mostly from the use of fossil fuels to run on-farm vehicles and machinery. Eliminating these emissions will involve replacement of diesel fuel by renewable electricity and clean hydrogen.

In each of these stationary energy subsectors, there are clear pathways to replace the use of fossil fuels with renewable electricity or clean hydrogen, so with determination, science and technology on our side, this sector will ultimately achieve zero emissions.

The transport sector is responsible for 18 per cent of our annual emissions; in the United States, it is a massive 28 per cent. While zero-emissions vehicles have been designed with flywheel and compressed air energy storage, the only serious contenders are electric vehicles, with the energy stored either in batteries or as hydrogen.

Battery electric vehicles

Battery electric cars have played a prominent role in transport twice in the past 120 years – in the 1890s and in the 1990s – but both times the internal combustion engine proved to be the fitter species, better adapted to meeting driver expectations. Today, new forces are at work shaping the environment in which cars compete and favouring electric vehicles over petrol or diesel vehicles. A kind of adaptive evolution has started to occur, with the rapid appearance of a new generation of electric vehicles that will replace the current generation of internal combustion engine vehicles.

The year 1899 was an auspicious one for mechanically powered vehicles. The 100 kilometres per hour benchmark was achieved for the first time. By an electric car! The car was named La Jamais Contente (never satisfied), and was driven by a Belgian, Camille Jenatzy. In 1900, 40 per cent of cars in the United States were powered by steam engines, 38 per cent by electric motors and 22 per cent by an assortment of primitive internal combustion engines. Let's call those electric cars at the turn of the century the first generation. By 1920, the landscape had changed dramatically: internal combustion vehicles dominated because of evolutionary advantages – the discovery of cheap oil in Texas and Pennsylvania, and the invention of the electric starter motor, which eliminated the physically difficult and somewhat dangerous hand cranking. Steam cars were effectively extinct, never to return, and electric cars had gone dormant.

In 1990, California adopted a zero-emission vehicle (ZEV) mandate, which many credit with launching a revolution in clean vehicle technology. The 1990 rule set an increasing quota for zero-emissions vehicles and sparked a flurry of development. Call these the second generation of electric cars. They were well built and loved by the few hundred drivers lucky enough to be lent a test vehicle by the car manufacturers. However, the lead acid battery technology was inadequate and the vehicles were pricey, limited in range and unreliable. The batteries took up so much room that even though the EV-1 passenger car from General Motors was a large car, it had room for only two passengers and the boot was too small for golf clubs. At the same time, catalytic converters and other clever design modifications conferred increased advantages to the internal combustion engine. In short, electric cars did not win the survival of the fittest competition at that time.

Around 2010, a number of electric cars were introduced to the market. They targeted a 160-kilometre (100-mile) range. Nice, but not good enough to alleviate "range anxiety." Call them the third generation of electric cars.

Finally, Tesla led the way, and we now have a growing number of electric cars that have a range of 400 kilometres or more, enough to eliminate range anxiety and come close to the range of petrol cars. Call these the fourth generation.

Battery electric cars are much more powerful than petrol or diesel cars, with a smoother start and huge low-speed twisting power at the wheels. For a driver, going back to a petrol internal combustion car after having driven a battery electric car would be like going back to watching a box television set after having become used to large-format flat-screen televisions. I don't know of anybody who has owned a fourth-generation electric car who has opted to go back to driving a V8 or any other internal combustion car.

They're also cheaper to run, with the price of electricity per kilometre only about a third that of petrol. And charging can be done at home, as easily as charging your smartphone, with the added benefit that you might only plug in once a week. I feel sorry for my friends who have to spend time on the petrol-filling ritual. My wife and I have had an electric car since 2013 and for most of that time we have charged the car in our garage from a conventional, 10-amp electric socket, exactly the same as that into which you would plug your desk lamp or your electric kettle. Slow and steady, you might say. Last year, we upgraded the outlet in our garage to a three-phase, 16-amp outlet. This is capable of charging a 400-kilometre range electric car from empty to full in about seven hours. Of course, public fast chargers can do that much more quickly, but we would generally only use a public charger if we were driving interstate.

Another cost saving for households that have solar is that they can charge their electric vehicles from the output of their rooftop solar panels. The average two-car metropolitan household spends $76 on petrol or diesel per week, or nearly $4000 per year. Two-thirds of that amount could be saved by shifting to grid electricity, or nearly the whole amount could be saved by shifting to rooftop solar electricity. This would dramatically reduce the total cost of ownership for the electric cars.

Today, electric cars are more expensive to purchase than similarly configured petrol cars, but analysts predict that the total cost of ownership will cross over in the next few years and the new-car purchase price will cross over a little later, certainly this decade. Combine the smoother and greater power, the low cost per kilometre driven and the convenience of plugging in at home, and even without the motivation to drive emissions-free, electric cars will overtake petrol cars. The momentum in the shift from internal combustion cars to electric is large and growing. It is clear from the daily announcements by car manufacturers around the world that they have seen the future, and that future is electric. Even General Motors, the company famous for its V8 super cars, committed in January of this year to phase out all petrol-powered cars and only sell zero-emissions cars by 2035. The company will spend US$27 billion over the next five years to this end.

Governments around the world are beginning to see the same future, and in some cases they want to lock it in to eliminate local air pollution as well as reduce carbon dioxide emissions. The United Kingdom announced in November 2020 that it will ban the sale of conventional petrol and diesel cars from 2030, and hybrid vehicles from 2035. In October 2020, China announced that by 2035 at least half of all new vehicle sales will have to be battery or hydrogen electric vehicles, while the remainder must be hybrids. In June last year, California adopted a first-in-world Advanced Clean Trucks rule to reduce the particulate and noxious air pollution from trucks driving past communities near freeways, ports and freight hubs; by 2030, 30 per cent or more of new truck sales across the size classes must be zero-emissions vehicles.

The outstanding transformation success story is Norway. Battery electric vehicles accounted for 54 per cent of all new cars sold in 2020, up from just 1 per cent of the new-car sales ten years ago. The national target of this oil-producing country is for all new cars sold to be electric in 2025. Norway is clearly well on the way, with predictions from the Norwegian EV Association that electric cars will account for 65 per cent of the market in 2021.

There are two common criticisms thrown at electric cars, neither of which withstands scrutiny. One is that they are unsuitable for towing. It is true that until recently manufacturers have not sold them with certification for towing, but that is changing – as with new cars from Audi, Mercedes, Jaguar and Tesla sold in the United Kingdom. The reason for the manufacturers' previous reluctance was that when the driving range was limited to 150 kilometres or thereabouts, the extra towed load would reduce the range to much less than that, severely limiting the potential for a drive to the country or the beach. With the much longer range of fourth-generation electric cars, this is less of a problem, and it will become even less so as battery capacity continues to increase. Indeed, a well-funded US startup named Rivian will next year introduce an SUV rated to tow 3.5 tonnes.

The other criticism I sometimes hear is that we should not be driving electric cars yet because the emissions from generating the electricity required to charge the car will actually be worse than driving an equivalently sized car. While that might be true in some coal-intensive states when comparing to a hybrid car, it is not the case when comparing to a conventional petrol car.

In any event, electric vehicles are the technology of the future. Across Australia our grids are rapidly decarbonising, and as grid emissions continue to reduce, the benefits of battery electric cars will further increase. For those fortunate enough to have rooftop solar for charging, the future of zero-emissions driving has already arrived.

Finally, the lifecycle emissions associated with manufacturing car batteries will decline as the energy supplies at the mines and factories approach zero emissions.

Hydrogen electric vehicles and vessels

The other type of electric vehicle is fuelled by hydrogen. The hydrogen feeds a fuel cell that does the reverse of the electrolysis unit that produced the hydrogen in the first place. That is, the fuel cell takes hydrogen from the car's tank, combines it with oxygen from the atmosphere, and produces two products: electricity and water vapour. The electricity drives an electric motor just like the electricity from a battery drives an electric motor, while the water vapour is released to the atmosphere.

In principle, the hydrogen could instead be burnt in the same way as petrol in an internal combustion engine, but for cars, trucks and trains, doing so turns out to be less efficient than converting it to electricity to drive an electric motor. Also, an electric motor provides a smoother driving experience compared with an internal combustion engine.

Here, the unsung hero is the hydrogen storage tank. Originally, storage tanks were made out of steel or aluminium and were limited to about 300 atmospheres of pressure. In 2001, stronger tanks were introduced. They are made from thousands of layers of carbon fibre wrapped round and round. They are not only designed to hold extremely high-pressure hydrogen, but also to withstand damage during a vehicle accident. To be certain, during certification testing they are subjected to fire and intense heat, simulated vehicle crashes, gunfire and explosions. They hold hydrogen at 700 atmospheres of pressure, the same pressure as seven kilometres underwater. They hold sufficient hydrogen for a hydrogen-fuelled medium-size SUV, such as the Hyundai Nexo, to have a range of more than 650 kilometres.

In electric vehicles, there is a battle brewing between batteries and hydrogen, but it is split between light vehicles, in which arguably batteries have the upper hand, and long-distance, heavy-haul vehicles, such as cross-country freight trains and cargo ships, in which hydrogen will likely have the upper hand.

Take two cars of the same size, one that uses hydrogen to store the initial electrical energy and one that uses batteries. For the same amount of initial electrical energy, the one using batteries will drive two and a half times further. So, when it comes to energy efficiency, batteries are the winner. But the more relevant price comparison for hydrogen is with petrol and diesel, as used in heavy vehicles. Per kilometre driven, hydrogen will soon compete on price with those traditional liquid fuels.

Hydrogen compensates for its efficiency shortfall compared with batteries through other characteristics. Start with light vehicles. If you have a home with off-street parking, there is nothing more convenient than a battery electric vehicle. However, if you live in an older terrace house with no garage, or a modern apartment that did not come with a car parking spot, having to find a public charger and wait for your car to charge would be consistently inconvenient. In those circumstances, and recognising that prices are falling, a hydrogen electric vehicle is an attractive option.

Now, look at large, long-distance vehicles, such as trucks that drive interstate, cross-country trains and international merchant ships. For these, batteries do not have sufficient energy storage density and so are too big to be practical. Hydrogen, and its derivative, ammonia, do. For example, I can envisage a bulk carrier ship taking 150,000 tonnes of iron ore from Port Hedland to Shanghai powered by ammonia or hydrogen, but I cannot imagine it powered by batteries.

It is likely that the use of batteries versus hydrogen will parallel the use of petrol versus diesel. That is, petrol for light vehicles, diesel for heavy vehicles; equivalently, batteries for light vehicles, hydrogen for heavy vehicles.

Hydrogen also has the advantage when it comes to recycling. Fuel cells will be disposed of and replaced no more frequently than conventional engines. The carbon fibre tanks to hold the hydrogen are just carbon, with thin plastic linings. There should not be any toxicity problem sending them to landfill. By contrast, batteries have a shorter expected lifetime, and their volume and the amount of raw materials required is significant.

What of shipping? International shipping is responsible for nearly 3 per cent of global greenhouse gas emissions, mostly from oil tankers, bulk cargo and container ships. The emissions are high because of the volume of cargo carried, not because individual ships are inefficient. On the contrary, a large ship emits just five grams of carbon dioxide per tonne of cargo carried one kilometre, which compares very favourably with 35 grams by train, 80 grams by truck and 435 grams by air.

In 2018, the International Maritime Organization set a goal of halving total emissions by 2050. This will not be easy because the volume of shipping has been steadily rising, increasing by more than 90 per cent from 2000 to 2018. Assuming continued growth, it will not be possible to achieve this fleet goal by incremental efficiency gains, such as the use of digital technology to minimise time spent waiting outside ports, increasing ship sizes, adding sails or using streams of bubbles to lubricate the hull and reduce friction. Instead, the fuel and engines will have to change.

Currently, large vessels use bunker fuel. This is the bottom-of-the-barrel distillate from refining crude oil. Bunker fuel is often so thick that it has to be preheated before it can be used. Many ships have shifted to using liquefied natural gas, which is a more efficient fuel and thus has lower carbon dioxide emissions, but a large number of those ships keep the LNG cool by allowing some of it to boil off into the atmosphere. This is a serious problem, because LNG is mostly methane, which is a potent greenhouse gas. For a proper solution, new ships are going to have to use a zero-emissions fuel.

The simplest way forward might be to modify the giant diesel engines to run on clean ammonia rather than bunker fuel. Finnish marine engine manufacturer Wärtsilä and German manufacturer MAN Energy Solutions have already started modifying their gigantic marine diesel engines to run on ammonia.

Smaller ships used for coastal shipping and inland waterways could use hydrogen directly rather than as an ammonia derivative. In this case, the hydrogen would power fuel cells to produce electricity to drive electric motors. The two biggest challenges are the lack of hydrogen refuelling infrastructure and the low volumetric density of hydrogen. The low density requires fuel tanks at least four times larger for liquefied hydrogen than for diesel or bunker fuel.

When it comes to transport, without question aviation is the biggest challenge. Aviation is responsible for nearly 2 per cent of global emissions. This is despite jet aircraft today being 80 per cent more fuel-efficient per seat kilometre than the first jets in the late 1960s. Unfortunately, there are no simple answers. Batteries are increasingly being used to power prototypes for short flights of a few hundred kilometres and a dozen passengers. But most of the greenhouse gas emissions in aviation are from the large long-distance planes that fly thousands of kilometres and carry hundreds of passengers.

One UK researcher calculated that an Airbus A380 that can carry 600 passengers 15,000 kilometres would be limited, if it used batteries and electric motors, to fewer than 2000 kilometres even if all the passengers and cargo were replaced with batteries. To see this limitation another way, consider the Boeing 787 Dreamliner. The flight from Perth to London takes seventeen hours, burning 92 tonnes of jet fuel containing nearly 1.1 gigawatt-hours of energy. If that amount of energy were carried in a battery, using the same kind of lithium ion batteries in a Tesla Model S, the batteries would weigh nearly 7000 tonnes, without even adding a requirement for an emergency reserve. This is vastly more than the fully fuelled weight of a 787 Dreamliner of approximately 220 tonnes, which is aircraft, passengers, luggage and fuel combined.

The most ambitious plan for long-distance zero-emissions flight that I am aware of is the Airbus goal to have zero-emissions aeroplanes flying by 2035, powered by dual thrust systems in which hydrogen in fuel cells provides electricity to turn electric motors that complement hydrogen used for direct combustion in gas turbines. These are concept aeroplanes at the moment, but intended to be capable of flights of about 4000 kilometres with 200 passengers. Time will tell.

Between them, the measures discussed above would eliminate 82 per cent of Australia's greenhouse gas emissions. After these, the march to zero is more difficult. What remains is agriculture, industry, waste and land use. Emissions in these sectors will take longer to reduce and will probably never quite get to zero. The pathways are unclear. Much more research will be required into new technologies, but there will also need to be new markets for waste management and recycling, and perhaps changes in food consumption. None of these is easy or predictable, especially behavioural changes. The residuals from these remaining sectors will need to be offset by geosequestration and biosequestration.

Agriculture contributes 67 million tonnes of emissions. By far the majority of this, 55 million tonnes, is methane emissions from cattle and sheep. The biggest source of methane in these animals is enteric fermentation, in which bacteria in the animal's stomach break down celluloses and other difficult-to-digest plant food. The by-product of these "methanogenic" bacteria is methane, which is released to the atmosphere when the animal belches.

So, what can we do? The amount of methane produced by each animal is influenced by the type and amount of feed it eats. All kinds of supplements are under investigation, including oils, fats, tannins, probiotics, nitrates, enzymes, seaweed and Australian native vegetation. Attempts have been made to use viruses to attack the methanogenic bacteria, and work is underway to develop vaccines against them.

The most promising approach is the work from our national science agency, the CSIRO. Scientists there have produced a feed supplement called FutureFeed, derived from *Asparagopsis* seaweed, one of the red algae widely distributed in Australian coastal waters. When added in small quantities of less than 1 per cent to cattle feed, it interferes with the methanogenic bacteria, and in published results it reduces methane production by 90 per cent and improves the rate of growth.

In December 2020, the CSIRO and collaborators James Cook University and Meat & Livestock Australia won the prestigious Food Planet Prize for their work to develop FutureFeed into a commercial product.

Of course, an alternative is behavioural change, where we shift from eating meat from cattle and sheep to non-ruminants such as pigs and chickens, and, of course, fish. Or plant-based substitutes or synthetic meat such as is being produced by Silicon Valley startups and now mainstream manufacturers. Synthetic meat, also called cultured meat, appeals to people who do not want to change their eating habits but prefer for ethical reasons not to be eating conventional meat, and for the possibility that it might be a pathway to lower emissions. However, on the latter, the jury is out. A 2019 paper by John Lynch and Raymond Pierrehumbert from the University of Oxford concluded that producing synthetic meat involves considerable emissions, and its emissions superiority to beef, if any, will depend on the carbon lifecycle efficiency of the scaled-up production systems.

The reality is that nothing is simple when it comes to emissions from agriculture. Even humble rice is a problem: methane from the anerobic decay of plant matter in flooded rice fields is estimated to contribute 1.5 per cent of global greenhouse gas emissions. Reducing this is an area of active research.

Industrial processes contribute 34 million tonnes of emissions. Of these, 13 million are from the leakage of hydrofluorocarbons, mainly from refrigeration and air-conditioning equipment. Hydrofluorocarbons became the refrigerant of choice under the 1987 Montreal Protocol, to replace the even more difficult to spell hydrochlorofluorocarbons and chlorofluorocarbons that were damaging the ozone layer. The replacement hydrofluorocarbons do not damage the ozone layer, but they are extremely potent greenhouse gases. An international phase-down was agreed in 2016, and in 2018 Australia started a gradual phase-down of hydrofluorocarbon imports. They will be replaced by other gases, such as ammonia, carbon dioxide, hydrocarbons and hydrofluoroolefins. The target is an 85 per cent phase-down by 2036.

The metals industry is the next most significant subsector, with 11 million tonnes of emissions. The majority of this, 7 million tonnes, comes from steel-making. As described, today's steel-making consumes large amounts of coal. Some reduction in the near term, perhaps this decade, will come from using natural gas instead of coal for the chemical reduction step, but in the long run it will be possible to eliminate the emissions from steel-making entirely by using renewable electricity for heat and clean hydrogen for the chemical reduction process. None of these process changes will be easy, and will require ongoing research, development and demonstration investments.

Carbon capture and storage will be needed in industrial processes that cannot otherwise eliminate emissions, or those in which the cost of capturing the carbon dioxide is essentially free, such as hydrogen production from fossil fuels. CCS is currently operational at large scale at nineteen industrial facilities internationally, including the Gorgon storage project in Western Australia. On the other hand, CCS has only been implemented commercially at two coal-fired electricity plants and only one remains operational.

Waste contributes 14 million tonnes of emissions. This is mostly due to methane generated by the decomposition of organic matter in landfills. Future reductions will derive from small decreases in the amount of waste sent to landfill, and increased capture of the methane to use as a fuel either for direct combustion or to generate electricity.

Land use and **forestry** contributed a net negative 18 million tonnes of greenhouse gas emissions in 2020. Emissions have been significant in the past, with forest clearing having had the worst impact, but trends have improved. Over the decade from 2008 to 2018, forested land in Australia increased by 2 per cent. In part this has been supported by the Commonwealth's Emissions Reduction Fund (ERF), of which 80 per cent has been allocated to increasing or maintaining vegetation cover.

Despite the most conscientious efforts, there will be residual emissions from industrial production and product use, agriculture, waste and land use. To achieve net zero, we will have to rely on negative emissions. That is, absorbing carbon dioxide from the air and storing it permanently. There are many ways to do this, but only three are seriously proposed.

The easiest by far is biosequestration, such as returning pastures and other farmland to native forests, or increasing the concentration of carbon-containing organic compounds in soils. The challenge here is permanency – that is, to ensure that the forests and soils will be protected and nurtured decades and centuries into the future. Biosequestration through forestation and afforestation is the only negative emissions technology to have been deployed at scale. It is supported in Australia through the ERF, which so far has contracts to sequester nearly 200 million tonnes of carbon dioxide from the atmosphere.

The second way is to grow and burn biomass to make useful energy in the form of heat or electricity, while capturing the carbon dioxide from the furnaces and permanently storing it deep underground. This approach is called bio-energy with carbon capture and storage, best known by its acronym: BECCS. The challenge for BECCS at large scale is cost and biomass availability. The Intergovernmental Panel on Climate Change (IPCC) has estimated the cost as between US$60 and US$250 per tonne of carbon dioxide permanently stored. More important is the price of the useful commodity, such as electricity. The International Energy Agency estimates the price per megawatt-hour as US$138 (A$180), which would require a substantial carbon tax to be competitive. While there are a few demonstration projects around the world, none is at commercial scale. The second constraint is the availability of low-carbon biomass. Growing, harvesting and transporting biomass involves carbon dioxide emissions that cannot be captured.

The third way to achieve negative emissions is direct air capture, in which carbon dioxide is removed from the air and permanently stored underground. The difficulty is that the carbon dioxide in the atmosphere is much more dilute than the carbon dioxide in the flue gases from an industrial process. For example, the exhaust gas from a cement plant might be 20 per cent carbon dioxide. Put differently, this is 200,000 parts per million. But the concentration of carbon dioxide in the atmosphere is only about 400 parts per million, or one carbon dioxide molecule for every 2500 air molecules. Thus, a lot of electrical energy is required to run the fans to pump the air to bring the low concentration of carbon dioxide to the collection membranes. The cost of the electricity is potentially very high, but we don't know because it has never been done at scale. Estimates vary from US$100 per tonne up to US$1000 per tonne of carbon dioxide captured. For perspective, note that the price paid under the Emissions Reduction Fund for carbon dioxide stored in biosequestration projects is typically under A$15 per tonne. Nevertheless, despite the current high cost, startup companies and even major oil producers such as Occidental Petroleum see potential and are investing in direct air capture with CCS demonstration projects.

As fate would have it, as Australia's chief scientist I worked on three government energy and technology initiatives. The first was the 2017 Independent Review of the Future Security of the National Electricity Market (the Finkel Review). Although the Clean Energy Target recommendation met its maker, the other forty-nine recommendations have either been implemented or are in process. Among other benefits, they have increased the capacity of the National Electricity Market to accommodate large quantities of solar and wind electricity without becoming electrically unstable. The second was the 2019 National Hydrogen Strategy, which is already helping to ensure a vital role for Australia in the international development of clean hydrogen as a fuel, energy carrier and industrial chemical. The third was the 2020 Low Emissions Technology Statement, which was the first instalment in the Low Emissions Technology Investment Roadmap.

Buckminster Fuller said: "You never change things by fighting against the existing reality. To change something, build a new model that makes the old model obsolete." The Statement implicitly follows Fuller's maxim. It sets out a technology-led approach to driving emissions towards zero for the long term, by helping low-emissions technologies become cost-competitive with the high-emissions incumbents. For example, if zero-emissions aluminium can be produced at the same price as today's high-emissions aluminium, purchasers will line up for the newcomer. Conventionally produced aluminium will become obsolete. If we achieve this tipping point by design, then, borrowing a term from 1950s marketing, we could call the approach "planned obsolescence."

My personal vision for a future, net-zero-emissions Australian society is one in which technology is rapidly advancing to the point of our being able to have our cake and eat it too. Energy will be clean, plentiful and cheap, supporting jobs in manufacturing, agriculture and indeed all sectors of the economy. By investing in low-emissions technologies, Australia will simultaneously confront the environmental challenges threatening our nation and the world, while laying the groundwork for our long-term economic security and prosperity. The challenge of climate change will be turned into a moment of opportunity for technological innovation, scientific imagination and job creation.

Our existing hydroelectricity supplies will have been maintained and supplemented by vast quantities of solar and wind electricity, transported across the system by long-distance transmission lines, and firmed by batteries, pumped hydro and massive hydrogen storage. The supply of electricity from the national electricity network for new uses in transport and hydrogen production will reduce electricity prices per kilowatt-hour for consumers, because the fixed transmission and distribution costs will be shared over a greater number of kilowatt-hours used. No coal-fired electricity will be left in the system, but some residual peaking gas might still be used to make up for shortages for a small number of hours per year. We will have achieved what I call the Electric Planet.

The difficult-to-abate sectors of the economy will have been partially addressed by new research-driven technologies and practices.

Australia will have a significant energy export industry, sending renewable electricity by cable to near neighbours, as clean hydrogen or ammonia to countries far and wide, and embodied in value-added products such as steel, aluminium and fertiliser. As the rest of the world weans itself off coal and natural gas, our exports of those energy resources will be substantially replaced by clean-energy alternatives.

Our cars, trucks, trains and coastal ships will run on zero-emissions fuels, such as electricity stored in batteries, clean hydrogen or ammonia. The price of equivalently configured electric cars will be cheaper than the petrol and diesel cars they replace, and their performance will be superior. Convenience will be high, because of the long range of the vehicles and the deployment of a national network of battery-charging stations and hydrogen-refuelling stations.

Our buildings, hot water, cooking and industrial heat will be powered by renewable electricity and clean hydrogen.

The chemicals industry will still be emitting greenhouse gases, but at a smaller level due to efficiency improvements and replacement by synthetic feedstock. However, hydrocarbons from oil and natural gas will continue to be needed. So, too, will agriculture be an emitter, but again at a smaller scale due to efficiency improvements, clean fertiliser and electric on-farm machinery. Just how much the agriculture industry can reduce emissions remains to be discovered.

Emissions from waste will be even smaller than they are today due to substantial improvements in recycling, and emissions from land use will be small or negative due to improved management practices.

The residual emissions from industry, waste and agriculture will be balanced by substantial biosequestration and modest geosequestration, with biosequestration practices delivering native forest and habitat regrowth, and more consistent farming yields. We will be a net-zero-emissions country and well respected for what we have achieved as part of the global effort to ensure that the measurements from Cape Grim will be grim no more.

We can do this, but it will take considerable effort and it will take time. So remember: be ambitious; be patient.

ACKNOWLEDGEMENTS AND SOURCES

An essay like this reflects what I have learnt from hundreds of colleagues and acquaintances over many years, but in particular for this essay, I thank first and foremost my wife, Elizabeth, for her penetrating questions and unwavering support. I also thank Kirsten Lawson for editorial advice and assistance; Amanda Caldwell and Sarah Brown for strategic support and resources; Chris Feik for editorial advice and probing questions; Will Howard for teaching me many aspects of climate science; Patrick Hartley for making sure that my enthusiasm for hydrogen never exceeded the need for accuracy; Tom Biegler for helpful insights into the energy required to run an all-electric Australia; Ros Gleadow for explanations about plant growth in high carbon dioxide atmospheres; Ben Wilson, Robin Batterham, Richard Bolt, Peter Tidswell, Rachael de Hosson, Matt Searson and Chris Johnston for reviewing and commenting.

4   1.4°C since national records began: Bureau of Meteorology and CSIRO, *State of the Climate 2020*, www.bom.gov.au/state-of-the-climate/, accessed 24 February 2021.

4   a ten-year-old: Bureau of Meteorology annual temperature series, www.bom.gov.au/climate/change/index.shtml#tabs=Tracker&tracker=timeseries, accessed 24 February 2021.

4   average global temperature: World Meteorological Organization, "2020 was one of the three warmest years on record", WMO website, 15 January 2020, Press Release Number 14012021.

5   approximately 90 per cent: Bureau of Meteorology and CSIRO, *State of the Climate 2020*.

5   Between 2006 and 2015: Rebecca Lindsey, 'Climate Change: Global sea level', NOAA Climate.gov, 25 January 2021, www.climate.gov/news-features/understanding-climate/climate-change-global-sea-level, accessed 24 February 2021.

6   CSIRO and Bureau of Meteorology: CSIRO, 'Latest Cape Grim greenhouse gas data', CSIRO website, www.csiro.au/en/Research/OandA/Areas/Assessing-our-climate/Latest-greenhouse-gas-data, accessed 18 February 2021.

7   measurements from the Mauna Loa Observatory: Global Monitoring Laboratory, Earth System Research Laboratories, "Trends in atmospheric carbon dioxide", esrl.noaa.gov/gmd/ccgg/trends/, accessed 18 February 2021.

8   "just over 0.04 per cent": Bureau of Meteorology and CSIRO, *State of the Climate 2020*.

8   average temperature would increase: Henning Rodhe, Robert Charlson and Elisabeth Crawford, "Svante Arrhenius and the Greenhouse Effect", *Ambio*, vol. 26, no. 1, February 1997.

11   bushfires of 2019 and 2020 in California: Michael Goss et al., "Climate change is increasing the likelihood of extreme autumn wildfire conditions across California", *Environmental Research Letters*, vol. 15, no. 9, 2020.

12   Field trials: Stephen P. Long et al., "Science, "Food for Thought: Lower-Than-Expected Crop Yield Stimulation with Rising CO_2 Concentrations", *Science*, vol. 312, no. 5782, 30 June 2006, pp. 1918–21.

15   once we find a source: Richard Smalley, *Our Energy Challenge*, Aspen Global Change Institute, 8 July 2004, www.agci.org/lib/our-energy-challenge, accessed 24 February 2021.

16   fuel economy for passenger vehicles: The shift to SUVs is increasing emissions. Laura Cozzi, "Growing preference for SUVs challenges emissions reductions in passenger car market", IEA.org, 15 October 2019.

18   "the virtuous cycle": Shinzo Abe, "Join Japan and act now to save our planet", *Financial Times*, 23 September 2018,

18   "a prosperous Australia": Department of Industry, Science, Energy and Resources, First Low Emissions Technology Statement – 2020: Global leadership in low emissions technology, Commonwealth of Australia, 2020 page 4. 18 December 2020 analysis: McKinsey & Company, *How the European Union Could Achieve Net Zero for Europe by 2050*, 3 December 2020.

18   Given the projected population growth: Projection of population to 2030 is 29.9 million. Australian Bureau of Statistics, "Population projections, Australia", 22 November 2018. The actual population in June 2005 was 20.3 million. Australian Bureau of Statistics, *Australian Demographic Statistics*, June 2005, cat. no. 3101.0, 9 December 2005.

29   To heat one litre of water: The charge of an electron is 1.6×10^{-19} so the number of electrons in one coulomb is $= 6.25 \times 10^{18}$ electrons. An amp is one coulomb per second. A kettle runs at 10 amps.

30   Total emissions: Department of Industry, Science, Energy and Resources, *National Greenhouse Gas Inventory*, Commonwealth of Australia, November 2020.

34   large hydroelectric dams: Catchment hydroelectricity describes dams filled by rainwater from a catchment area. The electricity from catchment hydro is a primary energy source. Contrast this with pumped hydro, in which electricity generated elsewhere in the system is used to pump water uphill to a dam, where it is stored and later used to generate electricity when needed. Pumped hydro is therefore not a primary energy source, it is a storage system.

34   Biomass, such as wood: Production of 546 TWh compared with total production of 26,730 TWh: IEA, "Bioenergy power generation", tracking report, June 2020, www.iea.org/reports/bioenergy-power-generation, accessed 25 February 2021.

34   Bioenergy in Australia: IRENA, *Renewable Energy Statistics 2020*, The International Renewable Energy Agency, Abu Dhabi, 2020.

40   "It is now cheaper": Silvio Maracci, "Renewable energy prices hit record lows", *Forbes*, 21 June 2020.

40   average price of solar electricity: IRENA, "Renewable power generation costs in 2019", 2020, https://irena.org/-/media/Files/IRENA/Agency/Publica-tion/2020/Jun/IRENA_Costs_2019_EN.pdf?la=en&hash=BFAAB4D-D2A14EDA7329946F9C3BDA9CD806C1A8A, accessed 18 February 2021.

40   cost of producing a megawatt-hour: Paul Graham, Jenny Hayward, James Fos-ter and Lisa Havas, *GenCost 2020–21*, CSIRO, Table B.9.

40   Wholesale prices: Australian Energy Regulator, "Quarterly volume weighted average spot prices – regions", www.aer.gov.au/wholesale-markets/wholesale-statistics/quarterly-volume-weighted-average-spot-prices-regions, accessed 18 February 2021.

40   For example, the Reserve Bank of Australia: Timoth de Atholia, Gordon Flan-nigan and Sharon Lai, *Renewable Energy Investment in Australia*, Reserve Bank of Aus-tralia, 19 March 2020, www.rba.gov.au/publications/bulletin/2020/mar/renewable-energy-investment-in-australia.html, accessed 18 February 2021.

40   price has been estimated at more: Victoria Energy Policy Centre, *Reality Check: Why CCS has no role in Australia's energy system*, https://243b2ed8-6648-49fe-80f0-f281c11c3917.filesusr.com/ugd/cb01c4_877c6ed2cc30435d8c90f951099494c7.pdf, accessed 24 February 2021.

40–1 Bluewaters coal-fired: Daniel Mercer, "Bluewaters coal-fired power station writ-ten off as worthless as renewables rise", ABC News (online), 18 December 2020.

43   It is widely estimated: Solar Cell Central, "Solar efficiency limits", Solar Cell Central website, http://solarcellcentral.com/limits_page.html#:~:text=The%2520Shockley%2520Queisser%2520Efficiency%2520Limit&text=The%2520modern%2520SQ%2520Limit%2520calculation,for%2520a%2520silicon%2520solar%2520cell, accessed 19 February 2021.

46   substitution method: This method is used by the Intergovernmental Panel on Climate Change (IPCC), the BP Statistical Review of World Energy, and the research and statistical aggregation site Our World in Data.

43   maximum theoretical: Centre for Sustainable Systems, University of Michigan, *Wind Energy Fact Sheet*, Pub. No. CSS07-09, September 2020.

49   By 2019 that had fallen: IEA, "Evolution of Li-ion battery prices", www.iea.org/data-and-statistics/charts/evolution-of-li-ion-battery-price-1995-2019, accessed 19 February 2021.

50   2017 study: US Department of Transportation, National Highway Traffic Safety Administration, *Lithium-Ion Battery Safety Issues for Electric and Plug-In Hybrid Vehicles*, DOT HS 812 418, 2017, www.nhtsa.gov/sites/nhtsa.dot.gov/files/documents/12848-lithiumionsafetyhybrids_101217-v3-tag.pdf, accessed 24 February 2021.

53   The round-trip efficiency of grid-scale lithium ion batteries: Environmental and Energy Study Institute, *Fact Sheet: Energy Storage*, 22 February 2019, www.eesi.org/papers/view/energy-storage-2019#1, accessed 24 February 2021.

53   Globally, pumped hydro storage: IHA, "Pumped storage hydropower", www.hydropower.org/resources/factsheets/pumped-storage, accessed 21 February 2021.

54   Between them: Australian Renewable Energy Agency, "Will pumped hydro unlock the transition to renewables?", *Arenawire*, https://arena.gov.au/blog/will-pumped-hydro-unlock-the-transition-to-renewables, accessed 21 February 2021.

54   22,000 potential sites: Will Wrights, "ANU finds 22,000 potential pumped hydro sites in Australia, ANU website, 21 September 2017, www.anu.edu.au/news/all-news/anu-finds-22000-potential-pumped-hydro-sites-in-australia, accessed 21 February 2021.

55   giant underground salt caverns or other natural repositories: National Renewable Energy Laboratory, *Energy Storage: Days of Service Sensitivity Analysis*, www.nrel.gov/docs/fy19osti/73520.pdf, accessed 21 February 2021.

55   Mitsubishi Heavy Industries: Jason Compton, "In Utah, hydrogen and salt domes are winning the west for renewable energy", *Spectra*, 22 September 2020, https://spectra.mhi.com/hydrogen-and-salt-domes-are-winning-the-west-for-renewable-energy, accessed 21 February 2021.

56   United States reducing its emissions: Perry Lindstrom, "Carbon dioxide emissions from the US power sector have declined by 28% since 2005", US Energy Information Administration website, 29 October 2018, www.eia.gov/todayinenergy/detail.php?id=37392, accessed 21 February 2021.

56   coal-fired electricity production fell: National Grid, "Britain hits historic clean energy milestone", National Grid website, 1 January 2020, www.nationalgrid.com/britain-hits-historic-clean-energy-milestone-zero-carbon-electricity-outstrips-fossil-fuels-2019, accessed 21 February 2020.

56   electricity from natural gas: Australian Energy Market Operator, *South Australian Electricity Report*, November 2020, Table 5 and Figure 16: https://aemo.com.au/-/media/files/electricity/nem/planning_and_forecasting/sa_advisory/2020/2020-south-australian-electricity-report.pdf?la=en, accessed 21 February 2021.

57   In the year to June 2019: Department of Industry, Science, Energy and Resources, *Australian Electricity Generation by Fuel Type*, 2019, www.energy.gov.au/publications/australian-energy-statistics-table-o-electricity-generation-fuel-type-2018-19-and-2019, accessed 24 February 2021..

59   "It will accelerate": Richard Bolt, "The Chief Scientist's critics are wrong", *The Sydney Morning Herald*, 3 September 2020.

62   "Yes, but water decomposed": Jules Verne, *The Mysterious Island*, 1875.

64   "I was inspired to write": Alan Finkel, "The future of hydrogen fuel", *Cosmos*, 23 July 2017.

65   "hydrogen city": Innovation and Science Australia, *Australia 2030: Prosperity through innovation*, Commonwealth of Australia, November 2020.

65   we produced: Hydrogen Strategy Group, *Hydrogen for Australia's Future*, Commonwealth of Australia, August 2018.

66   If we were to export: Department of Industry, Science, Energy and Resources, *Resources and Energy Quarterly*, December 2020.

71   hydrogen would be competitive: Hydrogen Council, *Path to Hydrogen Competitiveness: A cost perspective*, 20 January 2020.

72   "Around the planet": COAG Energy Council, *National Hydrogen Strategy*, Commonwealth of Australis, November 2019.

74   Japan planned: "Factbox – Japan's green growth strategy", *Reuters*, 25 December 2020.

76   breakthrough invention: Michael Dolan et al., "Vanadium-based membranes for hydrogen purification: Scale-up and industry variation", CSIRO, https://publications.csiro.au/rpr/pub?pid=csiro:EP17719, accessed 21 February 2021.

77   "Australia has an historic opportunity": Tony Wood, Guy Dundas and James Ha, *Start with Steel: A practical plan to help carbon workers and cut emissions*, Grattan Institute, 10 May 2020.

78   Emissions from producing 20 million tonnes of aluminium: Australian Aluminium Council, "Sustainability", https://aluminium.org.au/sustainability, accessed 21 February 2021.

81   The transport sector: US Environmental Protection Agency, "Sources of greenhouse gas emissions", EPA website, www.epa.gov/ghgemissions/sources-greenhouse-gas-emissions, accessed 21 February 2021.

83   nearly $4000 per year: Budget Direct, "Car running costs in Australia, 2020", Budget Direct website, www.budgetdirect.com.au/car-insurance/research/car-owner-cost-statistics.html, accessed 21 February 2021.

83   in the next few years: BloombergNEF, *Electric Vehicle Outlook 2020*, https://bnef.turtl.co/story/evo-2020/page/3/1?teaser=yes, accessed 21 February 2021.

90   in published results: Robert D. Kinley et al., "Mitigating the carbon footprint and improving productivity of ruminant livestock agriculture using a red sea-weed", *Journal of Cleaner Production*, vol. 259, 20 June 2020.

91   estimated to contribute 1.5 per cent: Tim Searchinger and Richard Waite, "More rice, less methane", World Resources Institute blog, 16 December 2014.

93   estimated the cost: Alistair Doyle, "Extracting carbon from nature can aid climate but will be costly: U.N.", *Reuters*, 27 March 2014.

93   The International Energy Agency estimates: IEA, "Impact of a carbon price of USD80 per tonne CO_2 on the LCOE of BECCS:, www.iea.org/data-and-statistics/charts/impact-of-a-carbon-price-of-usd-80-per-tonne-co2-on-the-lcoe-of-beccs, accessed 25 February 2020.

94   Estimates vary: Giulia Realmonte, "An inter-modal assessment of the role of direct air capture in deep mitigation pathways", *Nature Communications*, vol. 10, 2019.

Hugh Riminton

Laura Tingle's splendid survey of Australia and New Zealand covers a lot of ground. Usefully, she addresses the great mystery of the two former colonies – their differing treatment of their indigenous populations.

Why was a treaty a foundational moment in New Zealand as long ago as 1840, when even today the subject remains taboo in Australia? It is an issue so fraught with suppressed rage there is not a barbecue in the country that could not be stopped by the mere mention.

The Treaty of Waitangi not only recognised Māori sovereignty over their lands and waters, it was negotiated and drafted in the Māori language by Europeans who had taken the trouble to learn it.

In his classic work *Pakeha Maori*, Trevor Bentley records treaty debates that were "attended by more than 2000 Māori and sixty chiefs." Acting as translators were some of the escaped convicts, deserters, whalers and adventurers who had found their way to New Zealand. One of them was Jacky Marmon – the son of Irish convicts in Sydney – who deserted the whaling ship *Sally* in 1817.

By the time he assumed his pivotal role at Waitangi, Marmon was not only acting as an interpreter for the chiefs but "vociferously opposed their signing the document," writes Bentley. Marmon believed European colonisation "would degrade" the Māori. After some lengthy debate, they rejected his advice.

Laura Tingle accurately observes that for 135 years the treaty remained a mere bauble, routinely ignored as land-hungry settlers arrived in increasing numbers. But it remained in the national imagination. Every child learned about it. Unlike Australia's shameful lack of curiosity about frontier violence, every Kiwi kid learned of the "Māori Wars" (later more neutrally reclassified as the "New Zealand Wars") between settlers and the original inhabitants.

Tingle is right to observe that "New Zealand has embraced its indigenous culture over the past thirty years – and become both comfortable with and proud of it – in a way we have not." This is clear in daily life.

When I returned to my old hometown of Christchurch in 2011 to cover the disastrous earthquake, it was striking how many city leaders used Māori concepts unselfconsciously to communicate with a largely Anglo-Celtic population.

Earthquake survivors were urged to look after their *whānau* – a concept of family much broader than the close blood relatives that still define the Australian ideal.

"*Kia kaha*," people were encouraged. "Be strong." It is telling that this Māori phrase became the touchstone for the city, both then and during the even more shocking mosque attacks in 2019.

Also telling was that in the hours and days after the mosque attacks, when Christchurch citizens came to lay flowers and pay their respects, I witnessed two spontaneous outbreaks of the *haka* – one from a group of senior school children, boys and girls. Laura Tingle makes note of it.

Australia has nothing to match it. The *haka*, best known to Australians as the ritual that precedes an All Blacks international rugby match, is used increasingly widely in New Zealand to release inexpressible emotion.

In 2015, at my old school, Christchurch Boys' High, the head boy Jake Bailey delivered the end-of-year address from a wheelchair. Bailey, just seventeen, was afflicted with Burkitt's non-Hodgkins lymphoma, a cancer so vigorous that in a matter of weeks he had gone from a fit young man to a shrunken figure, almost lost in his school blazer.

With great poise, he addressed the staff and his fellow pupils. He urged those who were leaving for the last time to "be gallant, be great, be gracious and be grateful." As he finished, the boys in the hall launched into a *haka*. As the last sounds faded, Bailey mouthed, "Thank you," and he was wheeled away. It is hard to do justice to the power of the moment.

I have seen the *haka* performed elsewhere, spontaneously, for a retiring headmaster and for fallen Kiwi soldiers. The latter lives on YouTube. You can see for yourself.

When I asked the man who led a *haka* outside Christchurch's Al Noor Mosque why he had done it, he said he was throwing out *mana* to all those suffering from the massacre. *Mana* is another Māori concept that defies simple translation but which every New Zealander understands. In this case, through the *haka*, the people were projecting their own empathy, their spiritual power and strength, onto a shattered community.

"Māori culture," as Laura Tingle notes, "is increasingly seen as New Zealand's culture."

For someone largely raised in New Zealand, but who has lived as an Australian for nearly forty years, I cannot help but lament our Australian impoverishment.

The Uluru Statement from the Heart says Aboriginal and Torres Strait Islander sovereignty "is a spiritual notion." It goes on: "We believe this ancient sovereignty can shine through as a fuller expression of Australia's nationhood."

Given a chance, how could it not?

New Zealanders have long since abandoned the pernicious notion that there is nothing to be learned from Māori culture. Māori concepts pervade daily life. Australians, on the other hand, remain overwhelmingly closed to the interior world or practices of our sovereign elders. One notable exception, after the bushfire horrors of 2019–20, was the sudden interest in Aboriginal mosaic burning techniques as a means to limit the largest fires.

It is time for Australians to look east and learn from our strange-vowelled cousins. We are nearly 200 years behind them. Surely it is not too early to start.

Hugh Riminton

Colin James

To turn Laura Tingle's question around: can Aotearoa/New Zealand learn from Australia? Or are we too different?

Most in each country think we are "family," an ethnic accident born of Britain's joint colonisation. Over two centuries, we have swapped people, turned bushland into farmland, developed similar accents, believed ourselves rough and ready, down-to-earth and sporty (even if not always sporting), and reckoned on a "fair go." We shared what Geoffrey Blainey called a "tyranny of distance" from Home – that is, Britain.

We have squabbled a lot, as a family does: over what we should do in wars and international politics, how to treat those of us who live on each other's turf and more. For much of the time from the 1900s to the 1970s, we spoke less to each other as countries than to Mother Britain, and when we did talk, Australia spoke down to its smaller cousin, at times even leaving the "NZ" off "ANZAC."

Then the two of us put together a model free trade agreement in 1983. Though we have not turned it into the promised single economic market, it nevertheless reaches far behind the border into a wide range of regulatory matters, including cross-recognition of professional qualifications. Some of our sports codes have developed single competitions. Mid-level bureaucrats talk to each other.

But the two countries are also foreign to each other. Aotearoa/New Zealand has a starkly different geology, seismology, topography, geography, climate, and native flora and fauna from Australia's. Those natural differences have over time shaped differences of demeanour and attitudes, most starkly evident in New Zealand's anti-nuclear policy at the heart of an "independent foreign policy."

We also have different indigenous histories. Britain insisted on a treaty of cession from Māori with safeguards – the 1840 Treaty of Waitangi. The treaty was disregarded for twelve decades from the 1860s, but in the 1980s it set Aotearoa/New Zealand on a long, winding path towards becoming a bicultural nation.

Māori animist culture and the British post-Enlightenment culture introduced by colonisation are formally equal and increasingly inform each other and therefore government policy and practice. Growing numbers of non-Māori learn the Māori language, *te reo Māori*. Māori names are increasingly used for places alongside the imported colonial names, as "Aotearoa" is added to "New Zealand." The country is only partway down that long path towards biculturalism, but so far it has not strayed from it.

Māori came from the Polynesian Pacific around 800 years ago, many tens of thousands of years after Australia's Indigenous people arrived. Other Polynesians, from islands that were at one time occupied by New Zealand, have immigrated over the past five decades in large numbers. Biculturalism and the Pasifika infusion have made Aotearoa/New Zealand a nation of the Pacific, no longer just in the Pacific. Australia is on the edge of the Pacific.

There is one other huge difference between the two countries: size. Australia is many times larger in landmass, population and economic output (not least due to its abundant mineral resources, a major factor in its higher income, which Kiwis crave and have migrated to Australia to get a slice of). Accordingly, attentiveness runs much more westwards than eastwards. Australian foreign policy only bothers about Aotearoa/New Zealand if it thinks New Zealand has gone off-track or can be useful – to Pacific security, for example. New Zealand's foreign policy cannot avoid Australia, to the extent that Australian policy is quasi-domestic policy in Wellington. The smaller economy needs the larger one to do well, even as China has loomed large. Australian firms like their subsidiaries and exports across the Tasman to do well, but they look north more than east. An honest New Zealand diplomat posted in Canberra will quietly tell you that a proposal from Wellington for a trans-Tasman policy or program only gets a positive response from Australia when it comes towards the top of a list of priorities determined by domestic interests. Consider the response to New Zealand's efforts to establish mutual recognition of dividend franking/imputation credits: Australia has rejected the proposal, because its short-term revenue needs trump the economic findings that, overall, Australia would benefit.

But, for all our foreignness, we are family. We both belong to that minority of countries that are liberal democracies. And we are in a minority within that minority – two democracies still functioning by the book, unlike the dis-United States, dis-United Kingdom and most of Europe. We are both aligned with old "Western" values based on liberty.

So, while of course Australia and New Zealand need to adopt good practices from wherever they crop up in a diversifying and rebalancing world (New Zealand formed the Small Advanced Economies Initiative in 2012 so similarly sized countries could share ideas and data), we can still learn from each other's cities, sub-regional and national governments, businesses, non-profits and researchers. A high-ranking official said to me of Laura Tingle's article that we should turn its central question around and ask what New Zealand can learn from Australia.

In a post-COVID-19 world, which is searching for new social, economic and international norms (Aotearoa/New Zealand is experimenting with "wellbeing economics"), our two open, flexible societies potentially have an edge, especially if we combine efforts.

We are not too different to learn from each other.

Colin James

Frank Bongiorno

It seems a lifetime ago, but I was there in the crowd at the Melbourne Cricket Ground on 1 February 1981, when Australian cricketer Trevor Chappell bowled the last ball of the match underarm. Even as an eleven-year-old, I didn't need the media to tell me that what the Australians had done was ugly. When conversation in the car ride home turned to whether it was possible, in a game of cricket, to hit a six against an underarm delivery bowled along the ground, Tanya, the lovely English migrant who used to take her son and his friends to sports events, said she was sure the great West Indian batsman Viv Richards would have found a way.

New Zealand National Party prime minister Robert "Piggy" Muldoon said, "[It was] the most disgusting incident I can recall in the history of cricket ... an act of cowardice, and I consider it appropriate that the Australian team were wearing yellow." Muldoon was never inclined to understatement, nor one to let an opportunity to kick the Aussies pass by, but the basic thrust of his opinion found some backing on both sides of the ditch in 1981.

The underarm incident was the emblematic event in the trans-Tasman relationship of my childhood, even once the nuclear ship controversy came along a few years later. New Zealand's stand against visits by nuclear ships – and therefore against visits by any US ships at all, because the United States had a policy of neither confirming nor denying their nuclear status – attracted admiration on the Australian left at a time when the anti-nuclear movement was strong and disillusionment with Bob Hawke over his pro-US foreign policy provided much of the glue holding Labor's Left together. Hawke couldn't stand New Zealand's prime minister, David Lange. He thought him a buffoon who had made a devil's pact by using the nuclear issue as a bargaining chip with which to appease his own party's Left as the fourth Labour government pursued radical free-market reform. Lange's frequently incompetent handling of the issue didn't help.

The bad blood left by these matters can easily obscure the remarkable closeness of the relationship between the two countries. Even as the underarm incident was doing its work, Australia and New Zealand were moving toward an agreement that would allow the free movement of goods and services between them. Citizens of each country already had the right to travel, live and work in the other, as they do today.

Laura Tingle's thoughtful Quarterly Essay is not merely valuable for bringing together a great many details about Australia, New Zealand and the relations between them: she also resists the temptation to imagine that New Zealand does in every way better than Australia. Australian progressives have been a bit this way about New Zealand in recent years. Their glance across the Tasman has often seemed superficial and simplistic.

The Australian progressive attitude to New Zealand has been driven by a number of things, many of which are discussed in Tingle's essay: New Zealand's greater independence of the Western alliance, its more humane approach to refugees, its more civil and consensual politics, its more frequent Labour governments and the overwhelmingly attractive image of Jacinda Ardern. There is no makeover that will ever turn "Scotty from Marketing" into a figure with Ardern's charm, celebrity and appeal.

Unfortunately, those who celebrate New Zealand's superior ways are not "details people." As Tingle suggests, the story is a complex one. When social reformers from other places – Britain, continental Europe, the United States – looked to the antipodes in the late nineteenth and early twentieth centuries, they often understood Australia and New Zealand together as forming a "social laboratory." In many respects, New Zealand was slightly advanced, instituting both women's suffrage (in 1893) and industrial arbitration (in 1894) a little ahead of Australia. New Zealand premiers of that era, such as John Ballance and especially Richard Seddon, were admired by the reformers of many nations, and the country's social policy attracted international attention and even emulation. Marilyn Lake has recently emphasised the extent to which American progressives such as Theodore Roosevelt engaged with ideas pioneered in both Australia and New Zealand, including the arbitration of industrial disputes and the living wage. Clare Wright has revealed the influence that Australian suffragists had on the struggles for women's voting in Britain and the United States.

Between 1935 and 1949, New Zealand's first Labour government was ahead of both Britain and Australia in extending its welfare state in the direction of a "cradle to the grave" system. Australia's Labor government did similar things between 1941 and 1949, although with greater hindrance from both vested interests and the Australian Constitution.

But the point is that the two countries, despite going their own ways as dominions of the British Empire from the first decade of the twentieth century, had much in common as highly regulated mixed economies and welfare states. The sociologist Francis Castles argues that they formed the "wage-earners' welfare state": a social order that sought to modify market outcomes in favour of the family by emphasising the "social deserts" of the male breadwinner via wages. And as the historian Melanie Nolan has suggested, both countries liked to present a classless, egalitarian, consensual image to the world, although New Zealand's commitment to this self-image was probably more dogmatic than Australia's.

Were these societies all they were cracked up to be? Mention of the male breadwinner should already alert us to a darker side. The antipodean democracies were willing to allow women to vote, but both were rather less enthusiastic about giving them opportunities comparable to those enjoyed by men – that is, opportunities to be educated or to earn a living.

They were also racist. Australia is notorious for its White Australia policy. Did New Zealand have its own version? It did: it's just that it was smart enough not to proclaim it to the world with quite the same level of enthusiasm as the Australians, as if it were a proud national brand.

There were other complexities in New Zealand. The anti-Asian racism New Zealand liberals and radicals shared with their Australian counterparts coexisted, in New Zealand's case, with a more respectful attitude towards the Māori. The intellectual gymnastics involved in this process of forging honorary whiteness were remarkable. There was a widely held theory that they were an Aryan people from India and therefore shared a common racial origin with white settlers. Australians played these kinds of games at times too, but they never took hold quite as firmly on our side of the Tasman. Tingle rightly points out that the Treaty of Waitangi also proved an efficient instrument for dispossessing Māori of their land, a process that occurred in Australia without the fig leaf of an agreement with the original owners.

As New Zealand's record on race indicates, there has been a pragmatism, even an opportunism, that underpins its idealism. Its government knew, when it banned nuclear ships, that New Zealand would receive the benefits of protection without the costs. It had been a similar story in World War II: Australia brought most (although not all) of its forces home to fight the Japanese in 1941 and 1942. New Zealand kept its troops in Europe, where they would participate in the invasion of Italy. Again, geography mattered: New Zealand's isolation meant it was safe from the Japanese. Still, New Zealand looked the more obedient and helpful child of empire, at Australia's expense, at a time when both countries valued their

Britishness. It is also revealing that Helen Clark told Tingle that New Zealand's remoteness made it less concerned it might face a *Tampa*-like maritime refugee incident, another matter on which New Zealand has gained considerable prestige at Australia's expense.

None of this makes New Zealand either especially venal or unusually hypocritical. But it should at least prompt some hesitation about making easy comparisons that are unflattering to Australia. Ardern and New Zealand have rightly won praise for their management of the pandemic, but New Zealand is an isolated archipelago with a population smaller than Queensland's, as well as a unitary state with a unicameral parliament. Even allowing for the effects of mixed-member proportional representation, matters ought to be simpler there.

The similarities between the two countries remain. New Zealand still ranks very well on the Human Development Index. The latest index data – recorded pre-COVID – has New Zealand at fourteen (up three places over the last five years) and Australia at eight (down two). But the economic story is increasingly one of divergence. In the great post–World War II boom, the countries' incomes were similar and New Zealand could boast – and did boast – that it had the third-highest living standard in the world in the 1950s. In more recent decades, it's a different story. New Zealand's productivity is low, and its incomes have fallen well behind Australia's. While both countries have benefited from China's spectacular economic rise, mining has had significant positive effects on Australia's economic prosperity, contributing to highly favourable terms of trade. But mining isn't only an economic phenomenon. It's a political, social and cultural one too. That difference between the two countries matters a lot, and it is discussed, if perhaps underplayed, in Tingle's essay. When the mining companies defeated Labor's proposed super-profits tax in 2010, they succeeded in presenting themselves as the custodians of the national interest in a manner that has bequeathed problems to the Australian political system that no politician has been able to navigate successfully since. This sets us apart from New Zealand: it's a far cry from some short-lived anguish over where *The Hobbit* would be filmed.

It's true that News Corp's domination of Australian media, and the lightness of Murdoch influence in New Zealand, helps to account for some positive features of the latter's political and cultural life, including the muted nature of its cultural wars. But I would place more stress on the distinctive role of mining in Australia's economic and political life. When Rio Tinto destroyed two caves at Juukan Gorge, it wasn't merely enacting a business decision. It represented a particular way of being Australian and dealing with the world – white, entitled, masculine, violent and acquisitive – that echoes resource-dominated economies elsewhere but also has deep roots in the nation's history. It resonates more widely in the country's cultural, political and corporate life.

Does this sound like the international image of New Zealand in 2020? Hardly, although economic pressures might eventually tilt New Zealand in ways that its progressive admirers will find unsettling, rather as its post-1990 industrial laws have been anything other than a model of labour rights recognition.

Still, the cultural differences between Australia and New Zealand seem greater now than at any time in the respective histories of the two countries. Despite Tingle's hope that we might be a bit more like New Zealand in some respects, the capacity of either country to see much in the experience of the other that is worth learning is arguably more doubtful than it used to be.

Frank Bongiorno

Ben McKay

Laura Tingle's latest Quarterly Essay, *The High Road*, begins in March 2020, when Jacinda Ardern announced New Zealand's long and strong COVID-19 lockdown. Let's rewind four weeks from that moment to Kirribilli House in February. After three days in Fiji, Ardern was in Sydney, taking meetings with Gladys Berejiklian and Scott Morrison as part of annual trans-Tasman leadership talks. Of course, Ardern is no stranger to Australia. In the months prior, she holidayed in Queensland and made an official visit to Victoria. Australians have come to know her well, and they like what they see. A 2019 Lowy Institute poll revealed Ardern as Australia's favourite world leader – the politician Australians have the most confidence in "to do the right thing in world affairs." She topped the poll again in 2020. Outside Kirribilli in February, Ardern joined Morrison for a press conference with the Sydney Opera House in the background. It is a grand stage, and one Ardern used expertly.

After five minutes celebrating New Zealand's relationship with its "closest of friends," Ardern let rip. She whacked Australia's policy to deport criminals who hold Kiwi passports but lack links to New Zealand, saying, "Do not deport your people and your problems." This was far from the first time Ardern or her predecessors had taken aim at the policy, much loathed by New Zealanders, but it was the most brash, and the most direct, statement made so far. It was significant – and the reasons why are laid out in Tingle's essay.

Ardern's blast was never going to produce a policy shift. It was designed to show the New Zealand PM standing up to Aussie, to show leadership in an election year. On that count, it worked. Ardern's boldness left Kiwi observers picking their jaws up off the floor. It was out of character for the forty-year-old: Ardern's local political reputation as a consensus-builder and deal-maker, formed by cobbling together a coalition government with minor parties from both the left and right, and dealing with them on every issue in her first term.

The spray was also out of the national character. It is rare for Kiwi PMs to take their trans-Tasman counterparts to task. Ardern called the deportation policy "corrosive" in 2019, but she was almost deferential while doing so. Helen Clark maintained her diplomatic graces, even during the heated months of debate over the US-led invasion of Iraq, which Australia signed up for and New Zealand did not. And John Key was so complaisant he was given the Order of Australia by Malcolm Turnbull. ("Say it ain't so, bro," said Turnbull, when Key told him of his retirement from politics.) The only leader to show a degree of belligerence was Robert "Piggy" Muldoon, whose line about New Zealanders who depart for Australia raising the average IQ of both countries is quoted by Tingle.

Still, the sentiment expressed by Ardern was bang-on with public opinion. New Zealanders loved her attack. They blame deportations for growth in gang-related violence; they also find Australia's heavy-handed approach on this and other issues cruel. Whether it's for the unwillingness to support New Zealanders within the Australian welfare system (which New Zealand does for Australians), or the deportation of criminals with tenuous links to New Zealand (which New Zealand doesn't do to Australians), there is near-universal tut-tutting directed at Australia.

What has become clearer in my time as the New Zealand correspondent for Australian Associated Press is the mostly dormant exasperation of Kiwis towards Australia on many issues. Australians can tend to see New Zealanders as their poorer, more naive or simpler cousin across the ditch, and New Zealand as practically a state of Australia – with better skiing, better rugby players and that's about it. Naturally, Kiwis don't hold reciprocal views. And while New Zealanders hold little dearer than their down-to-earth nature and the manaakitanga, or hospitality, they show to outsiders, if you scratch the surface, you'll find a distaste for Australia – a latent but appreciable pique which sometimes breaks through. Tingle shows that this lingers within even the most sacred of bonds: the Anzac spirit. Outside Kirribilli, Ardern tapped the well of that sentiment.

Some further context: Ardern's attack came at the start of an election year, when New Zealand Labour's poll numbers were on par with those of the opposition National Party. Ardern's Labour would go on to win the election in stunning fashion, but not by playing to anti-Australian sentiment; Ardern announced the country's first case of COVID within an hour of the Kirribilli press conference. The imperiousness and global leadership she showed in handling the virus kept New Zealand from the worst of the pandemic and won her government a second term – without the need for coalition partners – in the poll on 17 October. It also repressed further analysis of her Kirribilli sledge, which, at the time, Ardern enjoyed. Roaring the RNZAF plane home shortly afterwards, she took a cup of tea down to the back of the aircraft to mingle with journalists, who were enjoying harder stuff after a week covering the PM abroad. The travelling press agreed Ardern and her team were fizzing from what they saw as a job well done.

But what next from Ardern and her government? Free from the constraints of coalition, and now governing in their own right, will Labour pursue a bolder path in its second term? Might New Zealand walk further away from Australia's policies on the areas explored by Tingle – on foreign policy, on climate change, on refugee and immigration intake, on indigenous rights? And does Ardern's assertiveness suggest an evolving trans-Tasman relationship – or was it a slice of election-year grandstanding (a charge Ardern's team rejects)?

Ardern certainly didn't hide her frustrations with Australia in her first press conference in Wellington's "Beehive" this year. On Australia Day, she fumed at Australia's call to suspend quarantine-free travel in response to a new community case of COVID. Ardern said she'd relayed her disappointment directly to Morrison, saying Kiwi officials had the situation "well under control," and it represented a fresh setback to the trans-Tasman bubble. That bubble was first agreed to last May, when Ardern attended an Australian national cabinet meeting. What does it say about the relationship that it took nine months to be enacted?

Thanks largely to the government's efforts in beating back COVID, Ardern enjoys unprecedented local popularity to match her existing overseas fandom. This may bring the government, and the country, more confidence and clout internationally. Labour's thumping election win certainly gives Ardern an unprecedented opportunity to implement her agenda. Relevant to Australia, one of her first post-election decisions was to appoint long-serving MP Nanaia Mahuta – known mainly for her activism on Māori issues – as foreign minister. At the same trans-Tasman leadership talks last February, Mahuta and Indigenous Australians minister Ken Wyatt inked a world-first bilateral "Indigenous Collaboration Arrangement." Mahuta is yet to put her stamp on the portfolio – aid could be a space to watch – and further indigenous association would be fascinating to see.

For all of these questions, what can't be doubted is that New Zealand and Australia will remain great friends. In times of tragedy – take the volcanic eruption on Whakaari/White Island, the 2019–20 bushfire season in Australia or the terrorist attacks in Christchurch – the two countries are there for each other. Still, Australia and New Zealand understand the world differently, and exist in it differently.

Unfortunately, Australian media outlets show more interest in covering New Zealand from Australian soil. While Kiwi companies tend to have Australian correspondents (and fine Kiwi journalists fill many Australian newsrooms), the ranks of Aussies in Aotearoa are diminishing. Just two Australian media companies staff New Zealand – AAP and Sky News. The presence of neither is guaranteed in the long term. The ABC has been without a permanent New Zealand correspondent since Dominique Schwarz left in 2014. COVID prevented other Australian journalists from in-person coverage of the two biggest stories of 2020: the sentencing of the Christchurch shooter and Ardern's thumping re-election.

Understanding Aotearoa can be of great benefit to Australia. Tingle's essay, a fine primer on the historical links and divergences between Australia and New Zealand, is also a strong argument for why Australian media companies should send journos across the ditch. The essay should be what they read on the plane.

Ben McKay

Tim Hazledine

I'm a New Zealander and an economist at the University of Auckland. I met Laura Tingle in Auckland in November 2019. I was impressed, of course.

However, when Laura told me that her next big project was to write a very long-form essay – an essay that would be published under the title *The High Road: What Australia Can Learn from New Zealand* – well, I wondered if the great Australian people were quite ready for that.

The essay – in itself, excellent – does not immediately soothe these doubts. And they seem all but confirmed by what follows in the same issue of Quarterly Essay: forty pages of commentary by nine people on Katharine Murphy's essay *The End of Uncertainty* from the previous issue, and a response from the author. The commentaries – which must all have been written just a month or so previously – are fluent, friendly and informed; all of them focus on the current Australian administration's response to the COVID crisis.

And the number of times the words "New Zealand" appear in those forty pages? Zero, zip, zilch. (The words "Jacinda Ardern" appear once, in passing.) I am not complaining. That would be hypocritical, given my own lack of learning about Australia. When I met Tingle, I think I may have implied or even claimed that the prime minister of Australia was a man named Michael Turnbull. Perhaps he was.

But anyway, why should the people of, say, Sydney care any more about goings-on in Auckland, 2350 kilometres away, than the people of London care about what's happening in Chișinău, the capital of Moldova, which is the same distance away? I note that our countries' governments have never had enough to talk about to support a viable direct air service between Canberra and Wellington (and, yes, there is a direct service between London and Chișinău).

Of course, an obvious difference is that anyone setting out in an eastward direction from London to seek commerce or companionship is likely to find it somewhere in Western Europe, long before they get as far as Moldova, whereas between Sydney and Auckland there is just empty sea – there's nowhere else to stop. So the relationship we do have, as the only Anglo countries in the Southwest Pacific, may just be a matter of *faute de mieux*, as we often say in New Zealand. And it's not even that we like each other. We pretty clearly don't much. Tingle's essay deflates the bubble of Anzac comradeship, quoting Australia's official historian of World War I, who viewed New Zealanders as "colourless," and another historian, who claims that Australians of that era saw New Zealanders as a "pale imitation" of themselves.

There's a lot of this sort of nonsense around. In World War II, a young British officer, Frank Thompson (brother of the social historian E.P. Thompson), after coming across antipodean troops in Egypt, wrote that "the New Zealanders are rough-hewn and intelligent; the Australians are rough-hewn and villainous." Perhaps the funniest put-down came from our dear departed John Clarke, a New Zealander who happily resettled in Australasia's only great city – Melbourne. When asked why he had left New Zealand, Clarke said: "Because it was there."

But all this is the reason Tingle *should* write her essay. If there is something for Australia to learn from New Zealand, who better – who at all? – to break through the apathy and antagonism than Tingle – author of three previous Quarterly Essays and held in the highest esteem in her country. Still, I am not sure that even she will succeed, but I will do my small bit to help by adding to her analysis of two topics – one on which I know a lot, one on which no one yet knows a lot, because it is an exciting work in progress.

The first topic is New Zealand's infamous "Rogernomics" episode of rapid, radical economic liberalisation over the seven years from 1984 to 1991. Tingle's essay is very good on why Labour finance minister Roger Douglas *wanted* to liberalise: he and his colleagues in Treasury genuinely and disinterestedly believed that massive "reform" would supercharge New Zealand's productivity performance. It's good on how they were *politically* able to do it: they were empowered by a combination of New Zealand's small size and its unicameral system of government, buttressed by less obviously disinterested support from the slightly sinister Big Business Roundtable lobby group. And it's clear about why the reforms were rammed through so quickly: they were quite openly aiming to get it all done and dusted before anyone could stop them.

But there's another notable dimension to this extraordinary episode. A list of the reforms implemented in those seven years is staggeringly long: more than 200 separate corporatisations, privatisations, liberalisations and so on, in both private and public sectors. How could a small, albeit honest, civil service – in a country of fewer than 4 million people – *administratively* deliver as many major policy upheavals as it most assuredly and successfully did? The answer is that implementing nearly every one of the 200-plus reforms was simply a matter of repeating the same basic formula over and over again.

Rogernomics is often casually claimed to be a textbook example of economic reform. Something to do with "free" markets. But it wasn't fundamentally to do with free markets, and the textbook had not been written, and still hasn't. The liberalisation formula – if mentioned at all – is buried away in the section of standard economic texts that deal briefly with issues of "asymmetric information," which arise when one party has knowledge that is not available cost-free to another. The formula is called the "principal–agent model," or just "agency theory."

The pervasiveness of asymmetric information in just about all social or economic interactions cannot be denied. We each know more about our own nature and actions than any other human being can. The issue is: what do we do with our private information? Agency theory assumes the worst: we will use our personal information advantage without scruple in our own narrow self-interest. I call this the "selfish shit" model of human behaviour. Its policy implications are stark. First, deflate the value of private information by removing from management anyone who actually knows something about how a business, a hospital or an industry works, and replace them with generic managers with no specialist expertise. Then write simple performance contracts for the new managers with narrow, measurable targets (key performance indicators, or KPIs) and incentivise them to meet those targets with carrots (bonuses) or sticks (the threat of dismissal).

This procedure could be (and was) rapidly deployed in just about every economic and administrative setting: from minding the money in the till of a cafe to minding the monetary policy of the nation. Employees were to be dissuaded from cheating on their employers by cranking up the threat of dismissal, which was achieved by weakening the trade union movement and increasing unemployment. The governor of the Reserve Bank of New Zealand had to sign a very simple contract specifying only that he keep inflation in a narrow, low band to get his bonus.

There are three big problems with agency theory in action. First, it's not that KPIs won't be met, but that they will be met at the expense of other worthy goals that didn't make it into the job contract – full employment, in the case of the central banker; willingness to act with initiative, in the case of the cafe worker.

Second, although the stark "selfish shit" assumption is factually false – in general, most people do behave in a trusting and trustworthy way – if applied long enough it can create the amorality it presupposes. If you persistently treat agents as untrustworthy, then eventually they may just say: "Stuff it. Why should I *be* honest if you aren't going to believe in me anyway?"

Third, a logic puzzle. If Roger Douglas believes everyone is a selfish shit, why shouldn't we believe the same of him? Why should we, the people, simply trust him – or anyone – to be our agent in these matters? "*Quis custodiet custodes ipsos?*" as we often say in New Zealand.

Well, to be fair, Roger did not trust himself – or at least he did not trust his successors. One of the reforms enacted slightly later is New Zealand's 1994 *Fiscal Responsibility Act*, which limited, in particular, the ability of the finance minister of the day to spend up big in election years, which practice had been shamelessly indulged in by all parties hitherto. Quite a good reform, that.

But, as a whole, Rogernomics has failed dismally, as Tingle documents. New Zealand's productivity, far from being supercharged, has spluttered along in Australia's wake, actually slipping further behind, with widening income inequality.

Why has there been no outcry, particularly from the protected precincts of university campuses? Well, the minority of academics who did speak out were treated with disdain or worse. In the mid-1990s, an emissary of the Big Business Roundtable came to the vice-chancellor of the University of Auckland and demanded that he fire New Zealand's most active public intellectual, the legal scholar Jane Kelsey, and "the socialist economist Hazledine." The vice-chancellor – an Australian – responded by promoting Kelsey to a personal chair and confirming tenure of my professorship.

The stupidity and viciousness of this little intervention was typical of the times and is still embedded in a strong rightist, conformist bias to New Zealand politics, including in our governing Labour party. Really, labelling a wishy-washy social democrat like me a "socialist" (not that there's anything wrong with being a socialist, of course) – because I am against monopolies and handouts to business – reflects what I hope Australians would regard as a rather distorted perspective.

The second topic of Tingle's I wanted to add to – the work in progress – is race relations. In 2011, I read a *New Yorker* article by Hilton Als on Jane Fonda. Als recounts the wedding of Fonda's son, Troy Garity, to Simone Bent, an actor. Garity is white, Bent black. The groom's father, Tom Hayden, a former Chicago Seven activist, made a speech saying he was particularly happy about the union because it was "another step in a long-term goal of mine: the peaceful, nonviolent disappearance of the white race."

If I had read this in, say, 1981, I would have responded: "Yeah, right!" But by 2011 – perhaps a little late – I was uneasy. I didn't, and still don't, give a fig about the disappearance of my race in a commingling of the bloods, but wouldn't that also mean the disappearance of the minority race – Māori, in New Zealand's case? And wouldn't the minority race have something to say about that?

Well, they did have something to say, and Tingle's essay is very good on the steps taken – in the nick of time – to regenerate Māori language and culture, particularly with the settlements that have been reached since 1987, supported by both political parties, through the Waitangi Tribunal hearing process. The slogan here is "self-determination," and (citing the Australian scholar Shireen Morris) Tingle summarises its outcome as the establishment of a "mostly comfortable biculturalism."

But what does biculturalism mean in this context? The term apparently originated in Canada, where it refers to the cordial separation between Anglo and French Canada: "two solitudes," as it was once described. I'd say that what is now happening in New Zealand is actually going in a quite different and very interesting direction – towards the building of a national culture that, perhaps uniquely in the world, is heavily influenced by the indigenous race.

Take the success of iwi-based Māori businesses, which operate commercially under a strong social charter – something which, according to Rogernomics, is not just undesirable but impossible. Our ongoing revolution in resource stewardship policy applies the principle that natural resources are "owned" not by humans but by themselves: *te mana o te wai* – the river owns the river, and the river has a right to be clean. The statement in Tingle's essay that "Māori culture is increasingly seen as New Zealand's culture": this is terrific, but it isn't about biculturalism – is it? Perhaps Australians can tell us.

Tim Hazledine

John Quiggin

Laura Tingle's insightful Quarterly Essay quotes my 2013 observation about New Zealand's approach to economic policy in the previous thirty years:

> During most of this period New Zealand has favoured free-market economic policies. Advocates of these policies have consistently predicted superior economic outcomes. In the early 1990s, for example, the late P. P. McGuinness suggested that New Zealand "shows every sign of being on the brink of overtaking Australia perhaps before the centenary of Federation in terms of living standards and economic performance."

Tingle goes on to observe that "the numbers tell a very different and brutal story about what happened in the New Zealand economy":

> New Zealand has not – as Paddy McGuiness prophesied – over-taken Australia in terms of living standards and economic performance. The Kiwi economy produces, and earns, way less per person than Australia. Incomes have fallen behind Australia's. The country has remained vulnerable to much more volatile swings than Australia. Inequality has risen sharply.

My response to Tingle's essay is mainly an amplification of her observation, looking in more detail at the paths taken to economic reform in Australia and New Zealand, and attempting to explain the sharp divergence in their economic fortunes.

First, it's worth stressing how badly New Zealand has done. Since the 1970s, Australia has remained in the middle of a pack of developed countries, including

Canada and most of Western and Northern Europe. By contrast, New Zealand is now more comparable to Mediterranean and Eastern European countries, such as Malta, the Czech Republic and Italy, which were much poorer in the past.

New Zealand has not only become relatively poorer, but more unequal. New Zealand was more equal than the OECD average in 1985, but the Peterson Institute for International Economics now ranks it as the third-most unequal of the OECD countries, as measured by the Gini coefficients – behind only the United States and United Kingdom. This is primarily the result of deliberate policy decisions taken by the reforming governments of the late twentieth century, reinforced by the National Party government of John Key.

The combined result of low growth and rising inequality is that low-income New Zealanders get a smaller share of a smaller pie than their counterparts in Australia (including New Zealand expats). Translating these results to the individual level, New Zealanders earn a median hourly wage of NZ$27, while Australians earn about A$34 (the two currencies are of roughly equal purchasing power). Moreover, because of the absence of a tax-free threshold, New Zealanders on low and moderate incomes pay more income tax than Australians. Finally, because New Zealand's GST does not exempt food, it is more regressive than Australia's.

In summary, whereas the standards of living in Australia and New Zealand used to be comparable, and very high by world standards, the average New Zealand worker is significantly worse off than their Australian counterpart, as well as being poorer than the average worker in most OECD countries.

New Zealand was not always a poor cousin. For most of our history, Australia and New Zealand moved in parallel – in economic development and in many other respects. As Tingle acutely observes, despite this close parallelism, neither one paid a lot of attention to the other.

In the aftermath of World War II, Australia and New Zealand were among the wealthiest countries in the world and the most egalitarian in terms of both social attitudes and economic outcomes. Indeed, a visiting academic (the American political scientist Leslie Lipson) observed that if New Zealand had a giant monument at the entrance to Auckland or Wellington Harbour it would be a "Statue of Equality" not a Statue of Liberty.

In power from 1935 to 1949, and led first by Michael Savage and then Peter Fraser, New Zealand's first Labour government established a modern welfare state. The Curtin and Chifley governments in Australia introduced similar measures. Yet few Australians would have any knowledge of Savage or Fraser, and the same applies to New Zealanders with respect to Curtin and Chifley.

The two countries followed parallel paths for several decades more: a long period with conservative governments in office, followed by short-lived labour governments, elected just as the world economy crashed in 1972 and then replaced by conservative strongmen (Malcolm Fraser and Robert Muldoon).

For both Australia and New Zealand, the 1970s were a period of deep concern about a perceived decline in relative living standards. As Western Europe enjoyed three decades of post-war prosperity (the *Trente Glorieuses*), and Asian countries – beginning with Japan – entered the "take-off" phase of rapid economic development, Australia and New Zealand fell back to the middle of the OECD pack on measures like GDP per capita. Australia's concerns at the time were reflected in book titles like *Poor Nation of the Pacific* and *Australia: The Worst Is Yet to Come.* In New Zealand, the future finance minister Roger Douglas offered *There's Got to Be a Better Way.*

In both countries, economic downturns at the beginning of the 1980s led to the return of labour governments, with leaders open to emulating the radical reforms that had commenced in the United Kingdom under Margaret Thatcher. As Tingle observes, this is where our story really takes off.

The general direction of the reforms undertaken in the early 1980s was already set by the time the labour governments took office. With the failure of the Mitterrand government's attempt to defy global capital markets, Margaret Thatcher's famous dictum that "There is no alternative" was more clearly true than at any time before or since. The deregulation of exchange rates and financial markets was unstoppable. That, in turn, implied the need for budget policies aimed at constraining debt and deficits, and therefore pressure for privatisation and cuts in public services.

There was, however, plenty of room for manoeuvre within those constraints. The Hawke government pioneered what was later called the "Third Way," which accepted the central tenets of Thatcherism, such as financial deregulation and privatisation, while maintaining, and in crucial respects enhancing, a redistributive tax-welfare system.

By contrast, the New Zealand Labour government implemented a market reform program more radical, in many respects, than Thatcher's, with little if any regard for the impact on its core supporters.

How to explain this difference? The fact that New Zealand was a unitary state with a unicameral parliament was important. But individual leaders also played a big role.

New Zealand prime minister David Lange was less interested in economics than in foreign policy issues like the ban on nuclear warships for which he remains famous. He acquiesced, at least initially, in the radical economic reforms proposed by Douglas and his allies, David Caygill and Richard Prebble. These reforms included deregulation, privatisation, and a goods and services tax with minimal exemptions and a rate of 10 per cent, which was soon increased to 12.5 per cent.

By contrast, Bob Hawke came to office with a plan to restore prosperity through a consensus between government, business and unions, which eventually became the Accord. While accepting the need for many of the reforms pushed by Paul Keating (Douglas's Australian equivalent), Hawke acted as a stabilising and moderating force. Most notably, he killed off Keating's plans for a GST, instead seeing the introduction of a fringe benefits tax and a capital gains tax. (When John Howard eventually pushed the GST through, food was exempted, and a 10 per cent rate was locked in, with a requirement that all states would need to agree to any increase.)

Unsurprisingly, in Tingle's words, Australian advocates of radical reform "looked wistfully, or at least with interest, across the Tasman," where the policies they advocated could be pushed through without regard to popular opposition. Whenever economic growth picked up in New Zealand, it was claimed that the Kiwis would soon overtake us.

As we have seen, the reality is far different. New Zealand has fallen far behind Australia and shows no sign of closing the gap. The divergence is too large and persistent to be explained by any one factor. Long-ago shocks like the entry of Britain into the European Economic Community should have washed out by now. Several possible explanations stand out.

First, it is now generally agreed that high levels of inequality are bad for economic growth. Whereas the efficiency benefits of a reformed tax system represent a one-off improvement, the costs of inequality keep mounting indefinitely. Any short-run gains in economic efficiency that may have been achieved by the reforms of the 1980s and 1990s have probably been more than cancelled out by now.

Second, New Zealand's macro-economic performance since the beginning of the reform era has been woeful. From 1983 to the beginning of the COVID-19 pandemic, Australia experienced only one recession, admittedly a deep one, at the beginning of the 1990s. New Zealand had five, including a deep recession which coincided with Australia's. Once again, this was a consequence of its reforms, which set a particularly stringent inflation target and discouraged any concern with unemployment.

More generally, the speed and ruthlessness of the reforms, which so attracted the admiration of Australian free-market advocates, entailed lots of collateral damage in terms of unemployment and social dislocation. At the time, it was assumed that any such damage would be more than offset by faster economic growth. Not only has that not happened, but it seems that some of the damage has been permanent.

All of these problems are amplified by the ease of migration to Australia. More than half a million New Zealand citizens (over 10 per cent of the total population) currently live in Australia, compared to around 60,000 Australians who live in New Zealand. Migration is driven by the gap in wages and productivity between Australia and New Zealand, but it also helps to entrench that gap. The failure of the reforms to increase living standards leads to a continuing outward flow of skilled and educated workers.

Most of the time, migrants are more ambitious and energetic than those who remain in their country of birth. These general tendencies are reinforced by the fact that New Zealanders are not, in general, eligible for unemployment benefits in Australia, which means that New Zealanders who lose their jobs have a strong incentive to return home.

Finally, what is likely to change in the future? My best guess is not much. Jacinda Ardern is an impressive leader in many ways, but it is already evident that she will do little to roll back the failed reforms of the past forty years. Despite the occasional use of socialist rhetoric, she shares the Third Way politics of Helen Clark and Tony Blair, both of whom she has worked for.

Ardern has promised to restore the 39 per cent top marginal tax rate, which prevailed under Clark's Labour government, and she has made some modest improvements in welfare benefits, but that's about it. Options like a capital gains tax and a wealth tax have been ruled out categorically.

Still, Ardern will be dealing with an economy in need of large-scale intervention if it is to recover from the disasters of 2020. In closing New Zealand's borders and locking the country down to eliminate the pandemic, she showed the capacity to take surprising and decisive action when it was needed. Faced with the prospect of further decline, and backed by an absolute majority in parliament, perhaps she will surprise us once again.

John Quiggin

Don Russell

I like Laura Tingle's notion that the similarities between Australia and New Zealand make our differences interesting. In a sense, comparing the two countries can be viewed as a controlled experiment. We are so similar in background and culture that wherever we have made different choices – either by design or accident – the difference in outcomes is powerful information that both countries should reflect upon.

Tingle is most insightful in her discussion of how the indigenous populations of the two countries have fared and how the countries have sought to deal with their distressing respective legacies. The evolving processes around the Treaty of Waitangi have been supported by New Zealand prime ministers over the years, who have dealt with community concerns and helped change attitudes. These efforts have meant that New Zealand has built something of a functioning bicultural country, which is now a recognised and comfortable part of the New Zealand national identity.

As Tingle highlights, Australia's response is more limited and confused. The path-breaking *Mabo* judgement from the High Court is progressing on its own complex track, but it has not triggered a process of national reconciliation or led to some form of national settlement, as the Treaty of Waitangi has done in New Zealand. As Tingle notes, there is no sense of national honour at stake in Australia, as has been the case in New Zealand, where Prime Minister Bolger said that when it came to Waitangi settlements the country was really talking about New Zealand's honour; Prime Minister Key regarded completing settlements as one of his greatest legacies.

The starting point for bringing a measure of justice to indigenous people tends to be community concern and political leadership, which prompts a legal response. This is understandable, as what is normally at stake are property rights and entitlements. Courts and tribunals are best placed to sit in judgement on such matters, away from winner-takes-all politics or "the tyranny of the majority," as the Americans say. Both New Zealand and the United States are fortunate that treaties were signed with tribal groups or nations in the nineteenth century. Those treaties did not stop both countries behaving as if *terra nullius* was the reality, but there was a readymade platform to restore lost property rights and entitlements when community attitudes changed in the second half of the twentieth century.

Community attitudes were also changing in Australia, but until *terra nullius* was overturned it was hard not to view Aboriginal dispossession and disadvantage through a social-welfare prism. While we should have been able to do better, it was almost impossible to build a basis for truth-telling or mutual respect. The High Court, in its *Mabo* and subsequent *Wik* decisions, changed all of that and established that native title survived European settlement and *terra nullius* was wrong in law. From that point, Australia had the basis for a new understanding or settlement with its Indigenous people. Whereas before they were a disadvantaged people treated very badly by history, they became a people with a High Court–sanctioned property right that had carried over from before European settlement. It was unclear what native title meant in practice, but the High Court had lifted the standing of Aboriginal and Torres Strait Islander people and breathed new life into groups that could demonstrate an ongoing link to the land. In this respect, we were moving down a path well known to New Zealanders.

As Tingle sets out in her essay, the key change in New Zealand was the 1985 legislation overseen by Labour prime minister Geoffrey Palmer, which allowed Waitangi claims to go back to 1840. This was highly contentious. However, as Tingle also highlights, it was subsequent National Party prime ministers Bolger and Key who made the legislation work. As conservative political leaders, they appear to have been attracted to honouring the legal rights enshrined in the treaty signed between the Crown and tribal chiefs.

In Australia, it was a Labor prime minister, Paul Keating, who made the Redfern speech after the *Mabo* decision and who then championed the *Native Title Act* through the Senate. However, unlike in New Zealand, there was little honour seen in delivering on the new-found native title rights established by the High court. Rather than an acknowledgement of the importance of the rule of law and the role of the court in protecting the rights of a minority in the face of potential majority opposition, there was widespread criticism of the court for going beyond its authority and usurping an authority that should rightly lie with elected governments. There was no acknowledgement that Australia's system of government – with its High Court, Senate, states and written constitution with enumerated federal powers – follows the US model. Or that Australia's founding fathers, by their actions, embraced the checks and balances built into the US system.

The American constitution reflects the deeply held view of the US founding fathers that democracy is not the election of George III. In embracing much of the US structure, Australia has gone down the same path. This can make life challenging for executive government in Australia, because authority is dispersed across the federal cabinet, the Senate, the states and the High Court. An Australian prime minister does not have the sweeping authority of a British prime minister, but our system tends not to have the fragility that political systems wedded to command and control often exhibit. By necessity, successful Australian political leaders bring people with them, and because we have a powerful High Court, we also have a mechanism to deal with highly contentious matters that no elected government could ever hope to address. Australia's system of government is not tidy, but political leaders have many pathways to success, which potentially gives Australia great capacity to change and evolve; when we do make big decisions, there is some confidence that those decisions have been appropriately scrutinised and assessed.

Tingle's essay can be seen as a tale about the negative consequences of winner-takes-all politics and how New Zealand decided to constrain the power of its prime minister and executive government, forcing it to operate with mixed-member proportional voting and coalitions of political parties. Tingle then marvels that, rather than creating paralysis, the New Zealanders have not only made it work but taught themselves the art of statecraft, as she calls it, to the point where Australian ministers and officialdom now look like amateurs. Her essay finishes with the triumphal re-election of Prime Minister Ardern.

My point would be that Australia never had a system of winner-takes-all politics and that in the past we have managed to achieve impressive and lasting policy outcomes because of that. Australia had to suffer the smirking condescension of New Zealand officials during the Lange/Douglas years as they watched the Hawke/Keating government patiently negotiate reform through the Senate, the Accord and with the states.

However, Tingle is right to highlight Australia's comparative failings with our Indigenous population. There was a time when Xavier Herbert's searing criticism of Australia — that it was not a nation but a community of thieves — could have been applied equally to New Zealand. Through collective endeavour and some inspired political leadership, this is no longer the case. Tingle's essay makes it clear that there is nothing stopping Australia from following New Zealand's example.

But it is not a one-way street, and I am sure Tingle would be the first to acknowledge there are areas where New Zealand can learn from the Australian experience.

I have in mind a common problem the countries faced in the 1990s: a low and declining household saving rate. Both countries suffered from low national savings, a heavy reliance on debt and a dependence on saving from the rest of the world through an uncomfortable current account deficit. Both countries gave high priority to reducing public-sector borrowing and saw merit in running budget surpluses to reduce the call on overseas borrowings and to free up resources for business investment and better domestic economic outcomes. However, at the time, only Australia took direct action to lift household saving. In 1992, Australia legislated to require employers to pay a proportion of every employee's ordinary time earnings as an additional payment into a superannuation account. This superannuation guarantee was initially set at 3 per cent, but over time it rose to 9 per cent. The guarantee is now 9.5 per cent and is legislated to increase to 12 per cent.

While the superannuation guarantee continues to attract debate, there is broad agreement that it has lifted national saving, a view that is strengthened by the fact that in 2007 New Zealand introduced KiwiSaver, a scheme also designed to lift household saving, albeit on a more modest scale. The history of household saving in the two countries is set out in the following chart. The data are annual and come from the OECD. The household sector also includes unincorporated enterprises.

Household saving: percentage of disposable income

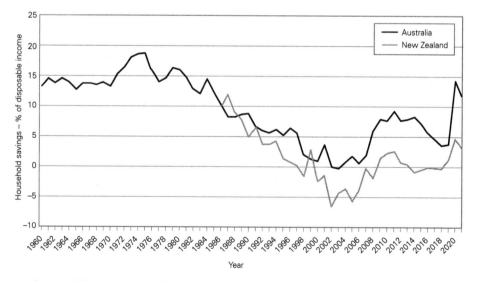

Source: OECD Economic Outlook No 106 (Edition 2019/2)

As can be seen, there was an alarming period before the introduction of KiwiSaver when New Zealand household saving was consistently negative. It was during this period that New Zealanders gained an international reputation as the worst savers in the OECD. While household saving has recovered in New Zealand, it is still tepid and runs at levels well below that in Australia.

English-speaking countries like the United Kingdom and the United States have long had a reputation for being excessively focused on current consumption, with low household and national saving. It is unclear whether this flows from cultural pressures to consume or easier access to credit, but this tendency for Anglophone countries to be low savers is recognised. With their low level of savings, both the United Kingdom and the United States have experienced low levels of investment, including investment in infrastructure. Over time, countries find that low levels of investment degrade their capacity to deliver for their citizens, and this has been a problem for both the United Kingdom and the United States. Fortunately, this is not where Australia finds itself.

As Tingle notes, New Zealand policy-makers feel some measure of frustration. They have embraced what would be regarded as conventionally good policy settings, but the outcomes have been ordinary. The New Zealand Treasury likes to benchmark New Zealand against other small but advanced economies. Unfortunately, labour productivity in New Zealand has fallen further and further behind that of others in this group. New Zealand has one of the lowest research and development intensities – both public and private – in the OECD. And perhaps most alarmingly, the Treasury acknowledges that New Zealand has "a long tail of low-productivity firms, indicating a lack of 'up and out' dynamics." Again, this is not where Australia finds itself.

With economics, everything is connected with everything else, and identifying causal factors can be complicated. However, if one reason had to be found to explain the performance difference between the two countries, it is hard to go past the quite different approaches that they have taken to retirement-income policy. Australia now has a superannuation pool close to A\$3 trillion in size. This large and growing pool of assets has led to the development of a range of competitive, innovative and large superannuation funds, determined to extract the best value for their members. Most importantly, there are now many large sources of patient capital in Australia. This has deepened Australia's capital market – a process that has helped fund Australian companies and infrastructure. It has also invigorated Australia's private equity market. Private equity has always been one of the drivers of innovative small businesses and startups in the United States. While the Australian private equity market has not reached the maturity of the US market, it has brought support and competitive tension to developing Australian businesses that would appear to be missing in New Zealand.

KiwiSaver seems to have made some difference, but with balances around NZ$60 billion it is still not large enough. Combined with a universal government pension, this has implications for New Zealand's budget and the dynamics of its economy.

Australia has a means-tested government pension, which means that as superannuation balances grow, there is some offset to government pension payments. At present, the Australian age pension costs around 2.7 per cent of GDP and is forecast to fall to around 2.5 per cent of GDP in 2038. The cost of the New Zealand pension was 4.8 per cent of GDP in 2015 and is forecast by the New Zealand Treasury to rise to 6.3 per cent in 2030 and 7.9 per cent in 2060. This is a big hole in New Zealand's budget and will put great pressure on other government spending, such as aged care and health. Moreover, the universal New Zealand pension is less generous than the Australian means-tested pension. As KiwiSaver balances are small, 40 per cent of New Zealanders retire with virtually no other income than the pension. The consequence is that New Zealanders see housing as their principal form of saving, further pushing up house prices and skewing investment away from productive areas of the economy.

As Australian superannuation funds explore investment opportunities in New Zealand, New Zealanders are beginning to focus on the design of the superannuation guarantee. The guarantee is compulsory and contains tax preference, because it is locked away until retirees reach the age of sixty. These features are missing from KiwiSaver, limiting its growth. There is also a growing realisation that Australia has a deeper and more sophisticated capital market than New Zealand because of the guarantee. And what really rankles is that while Australian superannuation funds are investing in expanding the New Zealand economy, New Zealanders remain mesmerised with housing.

As part of the controlled experiment that is New Zealand and Australia, New Zealand might want to look at the Australian experience with retirement-income policy.

Don Russell

Andrew Leigh

Visiting Te Papa, New Zealand's national museum in Wellington, our family stopped in front of a dramatic exhibition on the Treaty of Waitangi. "Where can we see Australia's treaty?" one of my young sons innocently asked.

Where indeed. As Laura Tingle points out, the lack of a treaty with the original inhabitants of this land is one of the areas in which Australia lags behind our antipodean neighbour. Across the ditch, Māori have dedicated seats in parliament, the All Blacks perform the *haka* at the start of rugby matches, and a government minister recently delivered an entire speech in the Māori language. Meanwhile, the Morrison government might have excised "young" from "Advance Australia Fair," but as Tingle points out, it has effectively downgraded the Welcome to Country and failed to deliver an Indigenous Voice to Parliament.

Alongside constitutional recognition, there are plenty of symbolic ways Australia could better recognise the first Australians. Inside the parliamentary chambers, Aboriginal and Torres Strait Islander flags could fly alongside the Australian flag. When parliament starts each day, the acknowledgement of country could be spoken in the Ngunnawal language. Capital cities could be given dual names. Instead of the Queen's visage, Australian coins could feature the heads of prominent Indigenous people (the $2 coin features the image of Gwoya Jungarai, but he is on the "tails" side of the coin).

It is not only on the issue of racial inequality that Australia could learn a thing or two from Aotearoa. When it comes to economic inequality, Tingle tells the story of its rise in the 1980s and 1990s but says less about its fall in New Zealand from the 1920s to the 1970s. When Tony Atkinson and I used tax data to estimate New Zealand inequality across this period, we found that the income share going to the top 0.1 per cent fell by two-thirds. In this egalitarian era, home ownership increased, and wages rose faster on the factory floor than in the corner office.

This was not an accident. New Zealand Labour's 1938 *Social Security Act* created a free health care system, introduced a universal family benefit and extended aged pensions. More public housing was built, and the eight-hour day was established, alongside other union achievements. That egalitarian tradition makes the sharp rise in inequality in the late twentieth century all the more shocking, as it tore apart a social fabric that had taken decades to weave.

Today, both Australia and New Zealand are considerably more unequal than a generation ago. Yet there is a thoughtful determination to reduce inequality in New Zealand that is absent in Australia. One valuable initiative is New Zealand's Integrated Data Infrastructure, a large research database that links together data from government agencies and surveys to better understand deep disadvantage. New Zealand researchers have used the database to explore the relationship between social housing and incarceration, between mental health and earnings, and between maternal services and childhood risk. In contrast to the Australian government's robodebt scheme, the database does not identify individuals: its aim is to inform structural reforms to help vulnerable people, not punish them.

Similarly, while New Zealand and Australia have similar rates of child poverty (around one in seven), New Zealand has made reducing child poverty a national focus. Not only is Prime Minister Ardern also the Minister for Child Poverty Reduction, but her government reports annually on the progress it has made on this issue. The analysis goes beyond money and includes estimates of the share of children who lack internet access (12 per cent), live in mouldy homes (8 per cent) and do not have their own bed (4 per cent). There is no reason to think these figures are better in Australia. And yet, since Bob Hawke's ill-fated pledge that by 1990 "no Australian child will be living in poverty," the issue has received far less attention than it merits in Australia. Scott Morrison isn't the minister for child poverty reduction, nor does he have one. Indeed, there's little reason to think that the issue would rank among the Morrison government's top 100 priorities.

In *The Luminaries*, a Booker Prize–winning novel by New Zealander Eleanor Catton, Crosbie Wells is writing back to his brother in 1854, explaining why he plans never to return to England. Naturally, he starts his letter by describing the weather in Dunedin: "The sun is bright on the hills & on the water & I can bear the briskness very well." But then he turns to social class: "You see in New Zealand every man has left his former life behind & every man is equal in his own way. Of course the flockmasters in Otago are barons here just as they were barons in the Scottish Highlands but for men like me there is a chance to rise ... It is not uncommon for men to tip their hats to one another in the street regardless of their station ... The frontier I think makes brothers of us all."

This brings to mind the nineteenth-century gold-digger who wrote from Australia back to England that "rank and title have no charms in the antipodes." The egalitarian tradition was a crucial part of the founding stories for both New Zealand and Australia. On racial equality, things are more enlightened today than in colonial times, yet there is much unfinished business. On economic inequality, the 50 per cent increase in the wealth of Australia's billionaires over the past twelve months is just the latest proof of the widening gulf between the rich and the rest. On both issues, Australians can learn much from our Kiwi friends.

Andrew Leigh

Shireen Morris

Laura Tingle is right that Australians should think more deeply about what our nation can learn from New Zealand. Her essay illuminates the parallel histories of two similar yet contrasting countries, grappling with comparable social, economic, political and cultural challenges in different ways. Most saliently for my work, New Zealand has implemented structural mechanisms for the recognition of Māori people, culture and heritage in ways that can provide inspiration for Indigenous constitutional recognition in Australia.

On Waitangi Day in 2020, Labor Opposition leader Anthony Albanese tweeted:

> We can learn a lot from our mates across the ditch about reconciliation with First Nations people. New Zealand has led the way. It's time for Australia to follow. It's time to support the Uluru Statement from the Heart.

Seven years prior, in 2013, former prime minister Tony Abbott (then the leader of the Opposition) similarly invoked New Zealand as a positive role model for Indigenous recognition. "We only have to look across the Tasman to see how it all could have been done so much better," Abbott said in a speech to parliament. "Thanks to the Treaty of Waitangi in New Zealand, two peoples became one nation." Here was conservative Abbott using the "T" word, pointing to New Zealand and calling on Australia to do better at coming to grips with our colonial history. It was no Redfern speech, but it was a moment of principled compassion and empathy. It didn't last.

In 2017, when Malcolm Turnbull dishonestly rejected the Uluru Statement's call for a First Nations voice as a "third chamber of parliament," Abbott also abandoned his support. For both leaders, compassion unfortunately gave way to political calculation. The Uluru Statement was sacrificed midst two men's self-interested tussle for power. At least Barnaby Joyce, who originally coined the misleading "third chamber" phrase, subsequently admitted the mischaracterisation and apologised "unreservedly." There has been no such honesty from Abbott or Turnbull.

Tingle is right that Australia was handed a momentous, generous gift with the Uluru Statement: the opportunity to undertake substantive yet modest and constitutionally conservative reform, to empower Indigenous peoples with a voice in their affairs. The proposal would give effect to decades of Indigenous advocacy for greater self-determination, while addressing conservative concerns about upholding the constitution. But as Tingle puts it, instead of accepting the gift, Australian political leaders "comprehensively stuffed it."

Despite that debacle, debate has rolled on. Public support for a First Nations voice has since grown. The 2020 Australian Reconciliation Barometer found that 81 per cent of the general community support the proposal (up from 77 per cent in 2018), despite past government negativity. Scott Morrison came to power promising an end to the "Muppet Show" and vowing to govern for the "quiet Australians." Given that polls indicate ordinary Australians can see the sense in Indigenous people having a constitutionally guaranteed say in laws and policies made about them, hopefully Morrison can succeed where Turnbull and Abbott failed. With goodwill and leadership, Morrison could be the conservative Nixon that can take this cause to China.

Lessons from New Zealand can assist in forging a path forward. In 2014, I was lucky enough to organise a research delegation to New Zealand with the Cape York Institute. We were awe-struck by the difference in political attitudes towards Māori recognition, displayed by both progressives and conservatives alike. I asked the then attorney-general, Chris Finlayson: "How is it that conservatives here respect the treaty and contemporary settlements so much?" He explained that conservatives believe in the rule of law and property rights. If the Crown breached Māori rights in the past, then it is only right that those matters are justly settled. It is about behaving with honour. Tingle correctly homes in on this word: honour. A quality too often missing in Australian politics.

Yet New Zealand demonstrates how political leaders can marshal difficult, painful and polarising debates about national identity and history in ways that diffuse, rather than inflame, the contemporary culture wars. Keating's historic Redfern speech was a masterpiece of oratory and an unparalleled call for Australians to have empathy in such matters. However, in retrospect, his repeated evocation of "we" – "We committed the murders. We took the children …" – may not have been the best way to facilitate consensus-building conversations about reconciliation. "We" can be morally confronting and can unhelpfully raise defences. It can be interpreted by some as an allocation of present-day blame for past wrongs. By contrast, Kiwis use the language of "the Crown" more than Australia, especially in matters of reconciliation. "The Crown" denotes the state, the government and political institutions. The Treaty of Waitangi, for example, was an agreement between Māori chiefs and the Crown, and breaches of the treaty are dealt with by the Crown. This language has arguably helped alleviate the sense that responsibility for past injustice must be borne by the present public: instead, "the Crown" takes responsibility and seeks to rectify past wrongs. In New Zealand, as in Canada, the idea of "the honour of the Crown" imbues dealings between Indigenous peoples and the state with moral gravitas and honour. This honour can similarly be ignited in Australia. We need not use the language of "the Crown" if it doesn't suit us. But political leaders can adopt language demonstrating that the Australian state is taking institutional responsibility for our shared history – to forge a fairer future on behalf of all Australians.

New Zealand teaches us that Indigenous constitutional recognition requires more than a static, symbolic statement. It requires more than a new preamble to the constitution, and more than a two-word change to the national anthem. True recognition involves dynamic, constitutional and structural reform to the relationship between Indigenous peoples and the state. Such reforms for Māori recognition and empowerment have been achieved over time. As Tingle explains, the Treaty of Waitangi was signed in 1840, but its promises were often breached by the more powerful Crown. As attitudes evolved, however, parliament pursued reforms such as the national Māori Council to ensure Māori a voice in Māori affairs and policy (similar to a First Nations constitutional voice), the Waitangi Tribunal and settlement processes (similar to the Uluru Statement's call for a Makarrata Commission to oversee agreement-making and truth-telling) and the gradual consolidation of Māori-reserved seats in parliament. As part of the Waitangi settlements process, formal Crown apologies are given for past wrongs – delivered in both Māori and English. Restitution can include some financial redress (though this is never commensurate to the real losses suffered) but also cultural recognition, including dual place-naming. The cultural component of the treaty settlements has propelled recognition of Māori heritage in a tangible way. The Māori language has been recognised as a taonga (treasure) under the Treaty of Waitangi, and as an official national language; the Māori Language Commission is charged with Māori language revitalisation.

New Zealand also demonstrates that rousing symbolic expressions can be important for national unity and pride, but they must sit alongside and complement the necessary substantive, structural reforms. Indeed, New Zealand has pursued both: the necessary institutional structures for Māori empowerment, complemented by the symbolic power that comes with true cultural embrace. As Tingle identifies, Māori culture is increasingly seen as New Zealand's culture. Witness the way in which variations of the *haka* are performed by New Zealand sports teams, including the All Blacks, as an expression not only of Māori culture and heritage, but also of New Zealand culture and heritage. By contrast, a few seconds of an Aboriginal war dance performed by Adam Goodes in 2015 prompted widespread contention in Australia. By some it was taken not as a celebration but as an affront, demonstrating that Australia remains uneasy with our national history and heritage.

From New Zealand we can learn that recognition can be mutual and cultural embrace can flow both ways. Pākehā embrace of Māori culture found a dignified role model when the New Zealand prime minister donned a traditional Māori cloak to visit Buckingham Palace, and when she gave her daughter a Māori middle name: Te Aroha, which means "love." Of the cloak, Māori weaver and lecturer Donna Campbell remarked: "To wear something that is so intrinsically of this place here and for her to wear it at that event, knowing that she would be photographed from every angle – that's a real acknowledgment of her relationship with the Māori people and with New Zealand." Māori experts advised this was not cultural appropriation, but a gift of honour bestowed on dignitaries. In Australia, Ken Wyatt, the first Indigenous Minister for Indigenous Australians, donned a kangaroo-skin coat to mark the occasion of his appointment. But how long will it be before non-Indigenous Australian politicians see fit to truly honour this country's First Nations heritage *and* implement the structural reforms that would see such heritage flourish – beyond the token words of Ngunnawal that Turnbull delivered in parliament the year before he rejected the Uluru Statement? Symbolic gestures mean nothing if not accompanied by substantive reform.

There are also constitutional differences that must be acknowledged. Achieving Indigenous constitutional recognition has arguably been easier in New Zealand than in Australia because of key contextual differences. Australia has a written, entrenched and rigid constitution, which can only be amended through a "double majority" referendum. By contrast, New Zealand's constitutional arrangements are not entrenched but enacted through ordinary legislation and conventions: a strong form of parliamentary sovereignty prevails, which entails constitutional flexibility. This has facilitated structural adaption and reform with greater ease. For example, New Zealand abolished its provincial system in 1877 and its upper house in 1950 via ordinary legislative change.

It has also facilitated reforms for Māori recognition over time, in line with changing political attitudes.

Another factor is the relative size of the indigenous populations. At 15 per cent of the population, Māori can wield a stronger political voice to advocate for such reforms. As a significant minority, they are probably harder for political leaders to ignore than Indigenous people in Australia, who represent 3 per cent of the overall population. A 3 per cent minority will always struggle to be heard, which makes achieving a *constitutionally guaranteed* First Nations voice all the more important in Australia – it should not be possible to abolish the institution as soon as it becomes politically unfashionable (as happened with ATSIC), although of course its institutional design should legislatively evolve as needed. In New Zealand, the existence of institutions like the Māori Council and reserved Māori parliamentary seats are anchored in principles of the treaty, which forged a sense of partnership between Māori and the Crown. Given Australia lacks a recognised founding treaty establishing such principles, a constitutional guarantee is needed to ensure a First Nations voice carries permanency and authority. Of course, the extreme minority status of Indigenous people in Australia also exacerbates the vastness of the comparative reform challenge. The Indigenous 3 per cent must persuade the general population that constitutional reform is a good idea. Yet this should not just be the job of Indigenous people: non-Indigenous people must help champion this cause too. But persuading the people is not enough. In addition to requiring a double majority referendum, section 128 of the constitution also makes parliament the initiator, and thus the gatekeeper, of any constitutional change. In reality, the roadblock to meaningful constitutional recognition in Australia is parliament, not the people.

On breaking through parliamentary blockages on progress, New Zealand also offers ideas for discussion. As Tingle notes, mixed-member proportional reforms were implemented in the 1980s after two "referendums" – what we in Australia would term plebiscites. These were ordinary political initiatives governed by a legislative framework, rather than constitutionally required referendums for constitutional change, as in Australia.

New Zealand regularly holds binding and non-binding referendums on national reform issues. In 2014–16, referendums were used to enable citizens to choose a national flag. In 2020, a non-binding referendum on the legalisation of cannabis was rejected by New Zealanders, while a binding referendum on euthanasia received strong support. Similarly, New Zealand's 1993 *Citizens Initiated Referenda Act* means any ordinary citizen can start a petition to ask for a nationwide referendum, and non-binding referendums can be held on any subject.

Non-constitutional referendums are not totally foreign in Australia: the same-sex marriage postal survey of 2017 was not the first time Australia experimented with a non-constitutional popular vote for a national policy question. In 1977, a popular vote was used to enable Australians to choose a national anthem – in contrast to the prime minister's perplexing unilateral decision to change its lyrics from "young and free" to "one and free" on New Year's Eve. Could a similar public vote, or even a citizen-initiated public vote, be a circuit-breaker on other important national issues – perhaps on a First Nations constitutional voice? Such a mechanism would not be binding on parliament (just as the same-sex marriage vote was not binding), but it could nonetheless help generate political pressure conducive to parliamentary action. A pre-referendum plebiscite may help persuade parliament to initiate the constitutional referendum.

Political leaders who want to connect with disengaged citizens should seriously consider such ideas. Recent research shows Australians want greater participation in government and in policy and law formation, especially on constitutional issues and matters of principle with which they can readily engage. The strongest support for greater direct participation is evident among politically disaffected citizens, suggesting the potential for citizen-based deliberation to enhance trust and participation in formal politics. With satisfaction with Australian democracy at historic lows and trust in political institutions in decline, perhaps Australia should take a leaf out of New Zealand's book and give citizens a more direct say in policy questions.

I think Australians would tell politicians to give Indigenous people a constitutionally guaranteed voice in decisions made about them. Because Australians understand it is the honourable thing to do.

Shireen Morris

Alan Atkinson

It was good to read Laura Tingle's Quarterly Essay comparing governments in Australia and New Zealand. It is high time that the two governments were set side by side like that, especially by someone who knows as much about both as Tingle does. There might be various methods of working out what is wrong with the way we in Australia are governed, but this is an excellent way to start.

Tingle's essay is a kind of twin study. The value of a twin study is that the subjects' original characteristics are as similar as possible, so that subsequent differences can be explained and addressed. In this case, the original characteristics of Australia and New Zealand certainly look pretty much the same: the two territories on either side of a single sea, each with indigenous populations, were occupied at about the same time by British capital, British military backup, and British methods of government, law and order, and they evolved into two independent nations that use the same language and moral idiom, participate in the same sporting competitions and belong to the same international networks. Sounds neat. It is, but it's only a start.

Tingle tells the story of the two countries' governments, mainly since World War II. She doesn't have much to say about their national origins, and she leaves scant room at the end for explaining why, when the countries so often do things the same, they do some things differently. It is as if she imagines writing another essay in which she might have the space to tackle these larger questions.

As it is, she takes a fairly narrow approach. She tends to focus on particular, bread-and-butter issues and on individual governing figures – their strengths, their virtues and their various agendas. She doesn't say much about underlying structure, the distribution of power at various levels or the mechanics of democracy. But then why should she? Isn't this precisely the point of her twin study? In these two countries, aren't these things pretty much the same?

Unhappily, they're not. Australia is a federation of partly sovereign governments scattered over a vast area, and it is technically a continent. New Zealand is a unitary state and very obviously an island nation. Tingle has almost nothing to say about the Australian states, and I think that's a pity. Towards the end of her essay, she mentions the possibility that strong and decisive government in Australia is hindered by the Senate (the New Zealand parliament has no upper house) and/or the states. However, she dismisses these explanations, opting instead for the argument that "political skill and leadership" is lacking. In other words, she seems to suggests that, with the right sort of skill and leadership, the complexity of the governing structure is beside the point.

And yet the relationship between complexity and leadership is surely more problematic than Tingle implies. It seems to me that Australian government and Tingle's essay have a problem in common. They're too top-down. They don't give enough space to the view from below – the sheer intricacy of life as lived and the urgent and increasing involvement of government in that intricacy. They don't engage enough with democracy – what it's for, how it works and how it's changing. That's an enormous gap.

The gap is particularly egregious given the direction of discussion about such matters overseas. In these years of fundamental revolution, the debate seems to be digging down to the human underpinnings of government, moving beyond questions of technique to questions of authority and its purpose – within the community and within the physical environment.

In this context, there's been a homing-in on questions of trust and truth. And then there's the question of economics, which is tied to the question of truth, because the prevailing economic theory, economic liberalism, depends so much on various types of fraud – misleading self-advertisement, which is the stuff of laissez faire, flawed theory and so on.

I miss, in Tingle's essay, the radical questioning to be found in the works of writers such as Naomi Klein and economics professor Mariana Mazzucato, who is director of the Institute of Innovation and Public Purpose at University College London. Mazzucato's book The Value of Everything (2018) surely ought to be a starting point in any discussion of future government in Australia. I also miss the sweeping demand for a renewal of democracy evident elsewhere – even in Joe Biden's manifesto as he takes on the presidency of the United States.

If Jacinda Ardern seems to govern more effectively than Scott Morrison, surely that's not just due to her political skill and leadership. It's not just because she's "actually nice" (Tingle's term). Kindness in politics – the consistent and useful kindness shown by Ardern – is not just a matter of smiling and hugging. It is a major administrative challenge. It depends on structural underpinnings and on keeping in touch with opinion and expertise on the ground. Effective government depends, in other words, on underlying organisational structure and everyone making the best use of it.

In Australia, the leading men and women in the debates on federation wrestled with these issues in the 1880s and '90s, when they were building up the structure of the new nation-state. All we usually remember of their discussions is what speakers said or implied about national identity, but they talked about a lot more than that. The most penetrating arguments circled around essential questions of trust and truth: how to create and sustain them, and what their place was in government.

The pioneering feminist Rose Scott argued fiercely against Australian federation. In spelling out her reasons, she put her finger on the problems that confront us now. Scott spent her life advocating legal and administrative reform to ensure the dignity and independence of women – in politics, in the workplace, in prison and at home. More broadly, she wanted to see power used differently at all levels, from the international to the domestic, with less reliance on violence and more on mutual respect and our capacity to listen. The union of the Australian colonies, she thought, was misconceived. It was driven by typically masculine arrogance, especially intellectual arrogance. In a federation fuelled by nationalist rhetoric, she said, "the voice of the people" would be lost. Everything would be concentrated on a system of power beyond the truths that men and women depend on in their daily lives and relationships. Government on that scale, removed from the jostle of common feeling, must be sterile, rigid and inhumane.

"The secret of all government is self-government," said Scott, echoing Thomas Jefferson. That included individual self-government. National self-government and individual self-government could only flourish together, Scott thought, in a transparent two-way conversation. How, she wanted to know, could that possibly happen in a country the size of a continent, and with a national government so remote?

A significant number of those who argued for the union understood this argument and tried to cater for it. Federation was their answer to the problem of remoteness. Since only the states could be democratic in a lively, ongoing sense, they had to retain real power, especially in the areas Scott was most concerned with: family, private property and so on. As the New South Wales politician Joseph Carruthers put it, there was "a decided objection ... to any federal interference with what the people conceive to be matters most sacred in the family."

In a genuine democracy, said South Australian politician J.A. Cockburn, most substantial government "should be within sight and hearing of the people," and in a united Australia the answer must be a carefully articulated layering of power. According to F.W. Holder (another South Australian politician), continental self-government and individual self-government would happily coexist under the new arrangement, because "every personal unit of the population shall be recognised and [their] individuality preserved." That would happen, Holder said, because "each state unit shall also have its individuality preserved and its independence assured."

I think Laura Tingle was mistaken in beginning the historical part of her discussion mainly with World War II. Our institutions have a resilience going much further back than that – and whether we understand them or not, they shape the way we behave. The Australian colonies had to be unified 120 years ago for various excellent reasons. A federal structure was the solution. But in forgetting the arguments that shaped the federating process, we also forget the profound connection – well understood at the time – between democratic process, multilayered power and good government. Today, if this connection is better understood in New Zealand, it might be because the multilayered part has always been so much simpler there.

"In my view," says Tim Flannery in *The Climate Cure*, "the federal government has proved itself incapable of properly administering drought funding and many other sorts of funding." Flannery doesn't mean just the current ministers. He means the federal government as an institution. State governments, especially the governments of New South Wales and South Australia, are running far ahead of Canberra in dealing with climate change. So are various local governments and, of course, the Australian Capital Territory. Could it be because governments at that level, like New Zealand, have a more fruitful relationship with democracy, including the lived and tactile democracy of community and place?

And what could be more instructive than government reaction to the COVID-19 pandemic in Australia, with state governments prioritising public and private health – calling for self-sacrifice and trusted input from all directions – while the federal government prioritises the centrally computed national economy?

But quite apart from recent crises, various administrative disasters over the years seem to prove, sometimes with wonderful neatness, that government on a continental scale has real difficulty in handling individual self-government, family matters and so on. The federal government has been taking over more and more of such matters since World War II. It's fair to say that in doing so it's often proved glaringly, and even cruelly, incompetent.

Individual self-government and "matters most sacred in the family" have fared especially badly among communities in Central Australia, thanks to a century of federal oversight. The conditions there, including entrenched poverty and degradation, do not suggest the government is "within sight and hearing of the people." However, it's the robodebt debacle that matches it most closely to the kind of government Scott foresaw, though more conscience-free and extraordinarily arrogant than even Scott could have imagined. The same pattern appears in the federal management of refugees, veterans' mental health, the NDIS, aged care and so on.

Tingle explains the need for Australia to compare itself with New Zealand, but New Zealand is already looking in another direction for useful comparators. In the last two years, New Zealand has formed a partnership of "Wellbeing Economy Governments" with Iceland, Scotland, Finland and Wales. The alliance aims to rethink the business of government altogether, focusing on the idea of "wellbeing economies" as distinct from GDP. (Mariana Mazzucato is on Scotland's Council of Economic Advisers.) If we take Tingle's advice seriously, Australia might eventually follow the same path. However, we would first need to resurrect the feeling for democracy that got the national project started in the first place.

Alan Atkinson

Bain Attwood & Miranda Johnson

Laura Tingle's Quarterly Essay seeks to draw out "point[s] of comparison" between New Zealand and Australia, two unusually interconnected and geographically proximate countries. Her aim is twofold: to raise the question of why Australians don't understand more about their smaller neighbour – though it is worth pointing out that Papua New Guinea is closer and probably even more misunderstood by most Australians – and to offer some examples of successful New Zealand principles, policies and practices from which she thinks Australians could learn. We welcome this essay because, as historians who have undertaken trans-Tasman comparisons, we also believe that comparative work can show us what we might otherwise be unable to see.

Why compare? Historians engage in comparison all the time, implicitly or explicitly. This can take various forms. For instance, we might draw analogies between present-day Trumpist politics and fascism in the past, as numerous historians in the American context have done over the past four years. In other words, we can compare in order to reveal *similarities* between the past and the present. Alternatively, we might undertake comparison in order to identify *differences* between nations (or other entities) and to isolate the truly important factors that caused those differences from the merely incidental ones. In order to learn from comparison, we must ask: what are the truly significant differences *and* similarities between the examples chosen, and what has *caused* those differences and similarities?

In our view, Tingle does a good job of describing a number of differences and similarities between New Zealand and Australia. However, we are left unsure about what Australia could learn from New Zealand, because she does not establish whether the differences between the two countries are in fact truly significant, nor does she provide a convincing account of the causes or sources of those differences. This has implications for what problems in Australia she thinks could be better addressed by attending to the New Zealand experience.

Miles Fairburn, one of the few historians to have recently undertaken comparative analyses of Australia and New Zealand, argues that it is difficult to make a strong case for New Zealand exceptionalism, because many of the phenomena that are claimed to be unique to New Zealand turn out, on close and careful inspection, not to be unique at all. As he argues, there have been many events in New Zealand's history that did not happen elsewhere, but a society with "an exceptionalist history is one where the history is composed of many events that are both unique (or highly unusual) and significant." Furthermore, an exceptionalist country "must not only experience a unique or unusual event but also take a divergent path from that of others in consequence." Exceptionalism, he argues, usually results from "very slow-moving forces" – and thus a structure that determines a "range of possibilities" in a country, "allowing some and preventing others" – rather than "faster medium-term social and economic trends and cycles" and "rapidly occurring short-term political events." Tingle focuses on short-term political events without providing a compelling case for there being significant underlying differences between Australia and New Zealand.

Tingle claims that the policies and practices used in the colonisation of New Zealand differed significantly from those used in Australia and led to a divergent appreciation of the value of indigeneity in the two societies today and thus major differences in the recognition of indigenous peoples' rights and the redress of disadvantage. In making this kind of claim, Tingle is by no means unusual. As the New Zealand historian Deborah Montgomerie pointed out more than twenty years ago, comparative projects often tend to exaggerate national differences and become exercises in either national castigation or national congratulation. This has certainly been true of studies of race and colonialism. New Zealand has frequently been compared with Australia, in both popular and scholarly discourse, in order to claim that Māori were relatively well treated. As Montgomerie has observed, "the good cop/bad cop school of comparative imperial history has been remarkably long-lived."

Yet if comparative work is to provide lessons for the future, it is vital that we pinpoint the causes of the problems being investigated as well as the reasons they have been tackled differently or similarly in the past. Otherwise, our suggestions for future change will be severely limited or badly flawed. For her part, Tingle claims that colonisation in Australia and New Zealand had very different "starting points"; she attributes this to the fact that Australia was "established on the legal idea of *terra nullius* – that it was unoccupied land when the British arrived – [and so] no thought was given to negotiating a treaty with the original inhabitants," whereas in New Zealand the British sought to negotiate a treaty with

Māori chiefs in regard to the cession of "sovereignty over their lands." In fact, she argues, "between *terra nullius* and the Treaty of Waitangi, it is hard to think of more opposite circumstances in which two places were settled."

Yet in 1769–70, James Cook claimed possession of parts of New Holland (what became eastern Australia) and New Zealand on the very same legal basis, namely the legal doctrine of *discovery* (not *terra nullius*). Moreover, it can be argued that if the British government had decided to plant a colony in the islands of New Zealand, or more especially the South Island, at the same time it did this in New Holland, it would *not* have sought to negotiate a treaty with Māori. Most importantly here, the making of the Treaty at Waitangi in 1840 was *not*, in and of itself, the reason Māori were treated as having some legal rights to land. New Zealand and Australian colonies such as New South Wales *did* have different beginnings in respect of the treatment of indigenous sovereignty and rights of property in land, but Tingle is unable to pinpoint, let alone explain, why this was so and how it has come to matter in recent decades.

More fundamentally, it can be argued, as Fairburn and others have done, that relations between white settlers and indigenous people in Australia and New Zealand did not actually follow a significantly different course after their beginnings, because they were both "the result of [British] colonisation, and wherever colonisation took place it led to the same fundamental outcomes, though not necessarily to the same degree: indigenous people lost their resources or autonomy or both."

Tingle occasionally, but only fleetingly, acknowledges this, as well as the fact that Indigenous peoples in both countries today experience social and economic marginalisation, and poorer health outcomes, longevity, earning power and educational attainment vis-a-vis non-indigenous – and particularly white – populations. Indeed, what is striking about the two countries, not least in the last forty years, is the degree to which their past neoliberal policies and practices devastated the livelihoods of many, especially indigenous people, in very *similar* ways. But Tingle is largely unable to grapple with and make sense of those similarities and instead exaggerates the importance of the countries' differences. Likewise, she seems at one point to grasp the paradox that much of the progress in recognising indigenous peoples' rights and attempting to redress their grievances occurred in both countries at the very same time that governments across the political spectrum undid a social contract premised on egalitarianism and a fair go for all – but she does not explain adequately why this was the case.

Tingle overstates the differences between Australia's and New Zealand's attempts over the last several decades to address the historical injustice that indigenous people have suffered. For example, at the same time as she acknowledges the similarities between the work of the Waitangi Tribunal in New Zealand and the National Native Title Tribunal in Australia, she makes the wild claim that Australia has barely sought to address questions about the status and rights of Indigenous people. Like many commentators, Tingle errs in claiming that Australia continues to suffer from a great silence or a cult of forgetfulness in regard to its relationship with Aboriginal and Torres Strait Islander people. There has been a great deal of historical truth-telling about this in recent decades (just as there has been in New Zealand). Similarly, Tingle ignores the fact that it is not only the New Zealand state but also the Australian one that has emphasised the importance of recognising the value of indigenous culture. What is more, she overlooks the deep, unresolved tension in both countries between claims for equality and claims for the recognition of cultural and political differences.

To be sure, there are important contrasts in the degree to which each country has sought to address historical injustice, but rather than simply attributing this to the presence or absence of normative moral, legal, philosophical and political forces in their governments, as Tingle does, it makes more sense to take note of the role played by material factors – for example, the fact that Māori are a much larger minority in New Zealand than Aboriginal and Torres Strait Islander people are in Australia, or that there was less post-war non-British migration to New Zealand than to Australia. Unforeseen consequences of government policies and practices must also be taken into account. For example, the New Zealand Labour government in 1985 had no inkling that granting the Waitangi Tribunal the authority to hear cases about historical breaches of the treaty dating back to 1840 would lead to a veritable flood of claims and the compensation of many Māori iwi (tribes).

In short, Australia and New Zealand *are* different in some matters – in shades of degree. But we will be better served by thinking of the similar and entangled histories of the two countries than by emphasising differences for the sake of drawing moral lessons. Such an approach might also help us to grasp the limitations of viewing the world through the lens of the settler nation-state and allowing it to stand in for all histories of the region. What happens to national accounts when we engage in comparisons between the pre-colonial indigenous histories of the two places, which in Australia stretches back 60,000 years and constitutes one of the earliest successful human migrations to a new land, and in New Zealand goes back around 800 years to the last of the great Polynesian *waka* (canoe) migrations to new islands? Or, as the historians Tim Rowse and W.H. Oliver have each asked, what happens to our take on the two nations if we consider intra-national regional differences (between north and south, east and west) much more seriously? And what of these countries' relationships to the broader regions of Southeast Asia and the Pacific? The yawning absence of the latter in how we see our past and future (despite our 21st-century demographic profiles) poses significant challenges to historians, journalists and other commentators, the majority of whom are white, often monolingual (or tutored in other European languages) and largely monocultural.

Bain Attwood & Miranda Johnson

Laura Tingle

Having now written four Quarterly Essays, I can say with some authority that they are beasts that sometimes get away from you. You start with one intent and learn a bit along the way, which sends you off in another direction – or, because you cover events that are still unfolding, you become hostage to that unfolding.

It's hard to peg down what you will and won't cover in these circumstances: in my third QE, for example, Donald Trump blasted through to dominate a discussion on leadership. In this fourth essay, it was a global pandemic.

Yet although COVID-19 meant I had to junk plans to look at a range of other debates in Australia and New Zealand – on savings, the political class and the role of business lobbies, to name a few – the focus of the work was always very clear. That is, I was not planning to write a comprehensive history of both countries, but to jump on the running boards of two countries already in motion, and to isolate a slice of time: the period marked by Britain's entry into the Common Market and the extraordinary, often parallel, changes that took place – partly as a response to that – in both countries.

I have been so heartened by the number of people on both sides of the Tasman who have said to me, "I never knew that" about something they read in the essay. And not just Australians talking about New Zealand, or Kiwis talking about Australia, but people of both nationalities talking about their own countries.

There is a great, rich vein to be tapped in intimate, comparative history. It forces us to look over the parapets, or to take a bird's-eye view of our place in the world. And the correspondence about the essay has been equally heartening in its embrace, for the most part, of the defined ambition of the essay and the quest of those of us in both countries to consider what we can learn from each other. Much of the correspondence also broadens the conversation, just as one would hope.

The reflections on indigenous affairs, in particular, show how rich a field this could be for our national conversation in Australia. Hugh Riminton – as a Kiwi and long-term Australian resident – is especially well placed to comment on how Māori culture has become embedded in his homeland, while Australia continues to fumble reconciliation so badly. And to illustrate how, in New Zealand, this is not just a matter of form, but also of substance.

Shireen Morris notes the importance of the structural mechanisms that have helped to produce this change and reflects on how, although Australian leaders on both sides of politics have invoked the lessons of New Zealand, we remain no further advanced in the debate. Now we are bogged down in a non-discussion about constitutional recognition – which is unlikely to see the light of the day before the next election – and other aspects of the Uluru Statement from the Heart have been brushed aside.

Morris is astute on how the language used by leaders can be so important in marshalling debates. For example, she describes Paul Keating's Redfern speech as "a masterpiece in oratory" but concedes that his "repeated evocation of 'we' – 'We committed the murders. We took the children …' – may not have been the best way to facilitate consensus-building conversations about reconciliation."

She contrasts that with the fact that the debate in New Zealand cited the obligations of "the Crown," which "denotes the state, the government and political institutions," rather than the populace at large. That obviously developed out of the history of the Treaty of Waitangi, but it might nonetheless point to a form of language that offers a path ahead in Australia.

Frank Bongiorno calls out the racism of both countries, and the particular contortions it has produced over the years, and he puts that racism in a broader historical context. I like his observation that "as its record on race indicates, there has been a pragmatism, even an opportunism, that underpins New Zealand's idealism. Its government knew, when it banned nuclear ships, that New Zealand would receive the benefits of protection without the costs." As he says, this doesn't make New Zealand particularly venal or hypocritical. But it gives us another prism through which to view our own bargains on such issues.

Ben McKay brings his authority and perspective as a political journalist for one of only two(!) Australian news outlets with full-time New Zealand correspondents. I was more than aware of the limits of my capacity to give this sort of insight, as someone who was dropping in from high altitude on the subject.

Tim Hazledine adds great ballast to the discussion with his observations about Rogernomics, corporatisation and the (often disastrously) formulaic approach to privatising more than 200 separate organisations.

He is right. To read the list of organisations that were up-ended, apparently without any great thought given to their individual markets or services, is quite shocking. As is reading the history of the sell-off process, in which a number of business figures were obscenely enriched and, because of the sheer smallness of New Zealand, too involved in what were clearly conflicting roles as advisers, sellers and buyers.

"Rogernomics is often casually claimed to be a textbook example of economic reform," Hazledine observes. "Something to do with 'free' markets. But it isn't fundamentally to do with free markets, and the textbook had not been written, and still hasn't."

While Hazledine focuses on the microeconomic reform record of New Zealand, fellow economist John Quiggin reflects on its macroeconomic record. As with indigenous affairs, these is a lot for Australian policy-makers to consider. Quiggin poses stark questions about many of the policy orthodoxies that have dominated the Australian conversation for much of the past forty years. As he says, the records show that "the costs of inequality keep mounting indefinitely," and – there is no kinder way of saying it – "New Zealand's macroeconomic performance since the beginning of the reform era has been woeful."

Quiggin is pessimistic about Jacinda Ardern's capacity to roll back forty years of economic change, however impressive her leadership has been during national crises. Nor is it a question of just starting at the end of the reform trail and rolling back. The mammoth, historic leap in the size of government intervention in response to the coronavirus – in both New Zealand and Australia – leaves policy-makers starting from a completely different point than even twelve months ago. You get the sense that there is some understandable floundering going on in Australia and New Zealand (and the rest of the world, for that matter) about where the policy discussions – and broader political axioms – will go next.

As a key player in the *Mabo* period and an adviser to Paul Keating, Don Russell has some fascinating insights into the indigenous debate. But his experience also gives him a particular view of the political game. He weighs my observations about how New Zealand has shifted its system away from the winner-takes-all executive dominance of the past with his observation that Australia has actually "managed to achieve impressive and lasting policy outcomes" because it was never burdened with that old system.

Russell, being the head of Australia's largest superannuation fund and intimately involved in the establishment of Australia's superannuation system, has great insights into the savings question in both countries. I'm pleased about this, because it is something I would love to have had the space to pursue.

Another area I would have been keen to pursue further is New Zealand's welfare policies, including its integrated data infrastructure, a subject raised by

Andrew Leigh. I remember hearing Bill English – still New Zealand's finance minister at the time – discussing his plans for reforms that would break the welfare cycle by judiciously investing in people early in their lives, rather than by punishment; he argued that this would save the budget billions in the long term. Sadly, as has often been the case, the Coalition picked up the idea in a ham-fisted way: it promised the savings and stinted on the investment. And it rushed the database that is at the centre of the New Zealand model. The result was the disaster of robodebt.

Laura Tingle

Alan Atkinson is an Australian historian. His books include *Camden*, *The Commonwealth of Speech* and the three volumes of *The Europeans in Australia*, the last of which won the Victorian Prize for Literature. He is now working on the story of the Macarthurs of Elizabeth Farm.

Bain Attwood is a professor of history at Monash University. He is the author of *Empire and the Making of Native Title: Sovereignty, Property and Indigenous People*, which compares Britain's colonies in Australia and New Zealand. He holds both New Zealand and Australian citizenship.

Frank Bongiorno is a professor of history and head of the School of History at the Australian National University. His most recent book is *The Eighties*.

Alan Finkel served as Australia's chief scientist from 2016 to 2020. He is a neuroscientist, engineer and entrepreneur. He led the 2017 National Electricity Market Review and the 2019 development of the National Hydrogen Strategy, and chaired the 2020 panel developing the Low Emissions Technology Roadmap. He is currently special adviser to the Australian government on low-emissions technologies.

Tim Hazledine is a professor of economics at the University of Auckland. He was previously a professor at the University of British Columbia and has held visiting teaching positions at the University of Warwick, Queen's University and Balliol College, University of Oxford. He is interested in economics as a social science and the policy implications that do and do not follow from this.

Colin James worked as a political journalist in Wellington for half a century from 1969, which included tracking the development and evolution of the Closer Economic Relations agreement. He participated in the Australia New Zealand Leadership Forum from its inception in 2004 until 2019. He has published eight books.

Miranda Johnson is a senior lecturer at the University of Otago. She is the author of *The Land Is Our History*, which examines the emergence and development of indigenous land and treaty rights claims in the Commonwealth settler states of Australia, New Zealand and Canada in the late twentieth century. She is a citizen of New Zealand and Australia.

Andrew Leigh is the federal member for Fenner and the author of several books, including *Battlers and Billionaires: The Story of Inequality in Australia*, and *Reconnected: A Community Builder's Handbook* (with Nick Terrell).

Ben McKay is the New Zealand correspondent for Australian Associated Press.

Shireen Morris is a constitutional lawyer and senior lecturer at Macquarie University Law School. She is the author of *Radical Heart: Three Stories Make Us One* and co-editor of *A Rightful Place: A Roadmap to Recognition* and *The Forgotten People*.

John Quiggin is an Australian Laureate Fellow in economics at the University of Queensland. He has produced more than 2000 publications, including seven books and over 250 refereed journal articles in fields such as decision theory, environmental economics and industrial organisation.

Hugh Riminton is the national affairs editor at Network Ten and author of *Minefields: A Life in the News Game*. He lived in New Zealand between the ages of five and twenty-two.

Don Russell is the chair of AustralianSuper, Australia's largest superannuation fund. He has extensive public- and private-sector experience and served as Australia's ambassador to the United States in Washington. He was principal adviser to Paul Keating during his time as treasurer and prime minister.

Laura Tingle is chief political correspondent for ABC TV's 7.30. She won the Paul Lyneham Award for Excellence in Press Gallery Journalism in 2004, and Walkley awards in 2005 and 2011. She is the author of *Chasing the Future: Recession, Recovery and the New Politics in Australia* and four acclaimed Quarterly Essays, *Great Expectations*, *Political Amnesia*, *Follow the Leader* and *The High Road*.

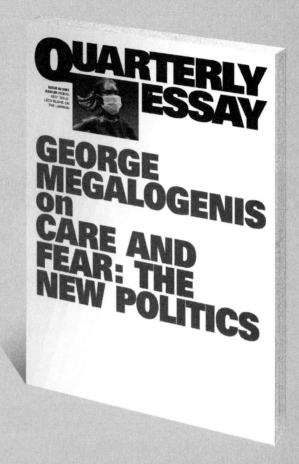

20 YEARS OF
QUARTERLY ESSAY

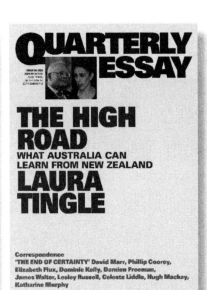

QUARTERLY ESSAY

THE HIGH ROAD
WHAT AUSTRALIA CAN
LEARN FROM NEW ZEALAND
LAURA TINGLE

Correspondence
'THE END OF CERTAINTY' David Marr, Phillip Coorey,
Elizabeth Flux, Dominic Kelly, Damien Freeman,
James Walter, Lesley Russell, Celeste Liddle, Hugh Mackay,
Katharine Murphy

QUARTERLY ESSAY

THE END OF CERTAINTY
SCOTT MORRISON AND
PANDEMIC POLITICS
KATHARINE MURPHY

Correspondence
'THE COAL CURSE' Zoe Whitton, Andy Lloyd,
Peter Christoff, Anna Rose, Tim Buckley, Stephen Bell,
Russell Marks, Judith Brett

**Subscribe to the Friends of Quarterly Essay
email newsletter to share in news, updates,
events and special offers as we celebrate
our 20th anniversary.**

quarterlyessay.com.au/signup

QUARTERLY ESSAY
BACK ISSUES

BACK ISSUES: (Prices include GST, postage and handling within Australia.) *Grey indicates out of stock.*

- [ ] **QE 1** ($17.99) Robert Manne *In Denial*
- [ ] **QE 2** ($17.99) John Birmingham *Appeasing Jakarta*
- [ ] **QE 3** ($17.99) Guy Rundle *The Opportunist*
- [ ] **QE 4** ($17.99) Don Watson *Rabbit Syndrome*
- [ ] **QE 5** ($17.99) Mungo MacCallum *Girt By Sea*
- [ ] **QE 6** ($17.99) John Button *Beyond Belief*
- [ ] **QE 7** ($17.99) John Martinkus *Paradise Betrayed*
- [ ] **QE 8** ($17.99) Amanda Lohrey *Groundswell*
- [ ] **QE 9** ($17.99) Tim Flannery *Beautiful Lies*
- [ ] **QE 10** ($17.99) Gideon Haigh *Bad Company*
- [ ] **QE 11** ($17.99) Germaine Greer *Whitefella Jump Up*
- [ ] **QE 12** ($17.99) David Malouf *Made in England*
- [ ] **QE 13** ($17.99) Robert Manne with David Corlett *Sending Them Home*
- [ ] **QE 14** ($17.99) Paul McGeough *Mission Impossible*
- [ ] **QE 15** ($17.99) Margaret Simons *Latham's World*
- [ ] **QE 16** ($17.99) Raimond Gaita *Breach of Trust*
- [ ] **QE 17** ($17.99) John Hirst *'Kangaroo Court'*
- [ ] **QE 18** ($17.99) Gail Bell *The Worried Well*
- [ ] **QE 19** ($17.99) Judith Brett *Relaxed & Comfortable*
- [ ] **QE 20** ($17.99) John Birmingham *A Time for War*
- [ ] **QE 21** ($17.99) Clive Hamilton *What's Left?*
- [ ] **QE 22** ($17.99) Amanda Lohrey *Voting for Jesus*
- [ ] **QE 23** ($17.99) Inga Clendinnen *The History Question*
- [ ] **QE 24** ($17.99) Robyn Davidson *No Fixed Address*
- [ ] **QE 25** ($17.99) Peter Hartcher *Bipolar Nation*
- [ ] **QE 26** ($17.99) David Marr *His Master's Voice*
- [ ] **QE 27** ($17.99) Ian Lowe *Reaction Time*
- [ ] **QE 28** ($17.99) Judith Brett *Exit Right*
- [ ] **QE 29** ($17.99) Anne Manne *Love & Money*
- [ ] **QE 30** ($17.99) Paul Toohey *Last Drinks*
- [ ] **QE 31** ($17.99) Tim Flannery *Now or Never*
- [ ] **QE 32** ($17.99) Kate Jennings *American Revolution*
- [ ] **QE 33** ($17.99) Guy Pearse *Quarry Vision*
- [ ] **QE 34** ($17.99) Annabel Crabb *Stop at Nothing*
- [ ] **QE 35** ($17.99) Noel Pearson *Radical Hope*
- [ ] **QE 36** ($17.99) Mungo MacCallum *Australian Story*
- [ ] **QE 37** ($17.99) Waleed Aly *What's Right?*
- [ ] **QE 38** ($17.99) David Marr *Power Trip*
- [ ] **QE 39** ($17.99) Hugh White *Power Shift*
- [ ] **QE 40** ($17.99) George Megalogenis *Trivial Pursuit*

- [ ] **QE 41** ($17.99) David Malouf *The Happy Life*
- [ ] **QE 42** ($17.99) Judith Brett *Fair Share*
- [ ] **QE 43** ($17.99) Robert Manne *Bad News*
- [ ] **QE 44** ($17.99) Andrew Charlton *Man-Made World*
- [ ] **QE 45** ($17.99) Anna Krien *Us and Them*
- [ ] **QE 46** ($17.99) Laura Tingle *Great Expectations*
- [ ] **QE 47** ($17.99) David Marr *Political Animal*
- [ ] **QE 48** ($17.99) Tim Flannery *After the Future*
- [ ] **QE 49** ($17.99) Mark Latham *Not Dead Yet*
- [ ] **QE 50** ($17.99) Anna Goldsworthy *Unfinished Business*
- [ ] **QE 51** ($17.99) David Marr *The Prince*
- [ ] **QE 52** ($17.99) Linda Jaivin *Found in Translation*
- [ ] **QE 53** ($17.99) Paul Toohey *That Sinking Feeling*
- [ ] **QE 54** ($17.99) Andrew Charlton *Dragon's Tail*
- [ ] **QE 55** ($17.99) Noel Pearson *A Rightful Place*
- [ ] **QE 56** ($17.99) Guy Rundle *Clivosaurus*
- [ ] **QE 57** ($17.99) Karen Hitchcock *Dear Life*
- [ ] **QE 58** ($17.99) David Kilcullen *Blood Year*
- [ ] **QE 59** ($17.99) David Marr *Faction Man*
- [ ] **QE 60** ($17.99) Laura Tingle *Political Amnesia*
- [ ] **QE 61** ($17.99) George Megalogenis *Balancing Act*
- [ ] **QE 62** ($17.99) James Brown *Firing Line*
- [ ] **QE 63** ($17.99) Don Watson *Enemy Within*
- [ ] **QE 64** ($17.99) Stan Grant *The Australian Dream*
- [ ] **QE 65** ($17.99) David Marr *The White Queen*
- [ ] **QE 66** ($17.99) Anna Krien *The Long Goodbye*
- [ ] **QE 67** ($17.99) Benjamin Law *Moral Panic 101*
- [ ] **QE 68** ($17.99) Hugh White *Without America*
- [ ] **QE 69** ($17.99) Mark McKenna *Moment of Truth*
- [ ] **QE 70** ($17.99) Richard Denniss *Dead Right*
- [ ] **QE 71** ($17.99) Laura Tingle *Follow the Leader*
- [ ] **QE 72** ($17.99) Sebastian Smee *Net Loss*
- [ ] **QE 73** ($17.99) Rebecca Huntley *Australia Fair*
- [ ] **QE 74** ($17.99) Erik Jensen *The Prosperity Gospel*
- [ ] **QE 75** ($17.99) Annabel Crabb *Men at Work*
- [ ] **QE 76** ($17.99) Peter Hartcher *Red Flag*
- [ ] **QE 77** ($17.99) Margaret Simons *Cry Me a River*
- [ ] **QE 78** ($24.99) Judith Brett *The Coal Curse*
- [ ] **QE 79** ($24.99) Katharine Murphy *The End of Certainty*
- [ ] **QE 80** ($24.99) Laura Tingle *The High Road*

Please include this form with delivery and payment details overleaf.
Back issues also available as eBooks at **quarterlyessay.com**

SUBSCRIBE TO RECEIVE
10% OFF THE COVER PRICE

☐ **ONE-YEAR PRINT AND**
   DIGITAL SUBSCRIPTION: $89.99

- Print edition × 4
- Home delivery
- Full digital access to all past issues, including downloadable eBook files
- Access iPad & iPhone app
- Access Android app

DELIVERY AND PAYMENT DETAILS

DELIVERY DETAILS:

NAME:

ADDRESS:

EMAIL: PHONE:

PAYMENT DETAILS: Enclose a cheque/money order made out to Schwartz Books Pty Ltd.
Or debit my credit card (MasterCard, Visa and Amex accepted).
Freepost: Quarterly Essay, Reply Paid 90094, Carlton VIC 3053
All prices include GST, postage and handling.

CARD NO.

EXPIRY DATE: /   CCV: AMOUNT: $

PURCHASER'S NAME: SIGNATURE:

Subscribe online at **quarterlyessay.com/subscribe** • Freecall: 1800 077 514 • Phone: 03 9486 0288
Email: subscribe@quarterlyessay.com (please do not send electronic scans of this form)